BYE BABY

BRIDGET REILLY'S INCREDIBLE TRUE STORY

DANIEL DONNELLY

CRAIC
PUBLISHING

First published by Craic Publishing in 2018

Perth, Australia

Paperback ISBN: 978-0-6482577-0-7

eBook ISBN: 978-0-6482577-1-4

Edited and typeset by Katherine Trail

Cover design by Andrej Semnic (Semntiz)

Cover Photography from iStock.com and Getty Images

© Craic Publishing

www.byebabybook.com

byebaby@byebabybook.com

This is true story. However, some names and details have been changed to protect the identities of those involved.

For mothers, young and old, married and unmarried, who've endured adversity for the love of their children.

IMAGINE BEING ABLE TO REMEMBER

Remember when your child was born?
That euphoric moment when they took their first gasps of life and their
piercing cries rang out for the first time.
Remember the warmth of their body against yours.
The smell of their skin.
The soft touch of their hair.
Their little nose, ears, and mouth.
Their tiny toes and hands, which were small enough to grip around
your little finger.
Remember watching your child grow, firstly when they became too big
for their baby clothes, then their crib.
Remember watching them crawl, then stumble, until they finally found
their feet.
Remember hearing their voice, which started out as incoherent
ramblings and little murmurs, before evolving into their first words –
'Mum' and 'Dad'.

Remember the way they looked up at you, their eyes wide with wonder, and the way tears filled those eyes when they yearned to be in your grasp.

Remember how your baby made your heart flutter, the way nothing else mattered when you held them.

Remember that feeling, being consumed by love and knowing you'd always love them — but more than that, knowing they'd always be a part of you.

Now, imagine having your child, your baby, that eternal part of you, taken away.

Imagine being told it's because 'You're not married,' and 'It's for the best.'

Imagine being shunned by family, friends, everyone, and being sentenced to a life of silent misery.

Imagine trying to fight to keep your baby, only to be denied and told 'You're being selfish.'

Imagine then trying to move on with your life, without your baby, with a part of you missing.

Imagine seeing children in the street years later, wondering if it's your child, because you don't know where they are, or who's raising them, or how they're being treated.

Imagine knowing you'll never see your child again.

For some mothers, too many mothers, they don't have to imagine. They remember.

Because their babies were taken from them.

Some were taken after weeks of mother–baby bonding; others were snatched at birth.

And all of this happened not so long ago.

It could have happened to your mother or your grandmother.

So, why should we now remember this painful past?

We must remember, to allow unmarried mothers and their children the chance to be heard, to show them they're not forgotten any more.
We must remember, to give them the chance to heal.
And we must remember, so we make sure this never happens again.

PRESENT

CHAPTER ONE

MY MOTHER'S SECRET

Her blue eyes are already glassy. They're glistening under the golden lights that hang from her kitchen ceiling. We sit at her oak dining table, steam rising from fresh cups of tea in front of us. She unfolds a thick stack of papers that are covered from top to bottom in messy blue handwriting. She's written it on paper. Of course she has. I don't think I've ever seen her use a computer, plus she doesn't own a printer, or an iPad. She inhales deeply and half-smiles at me through a closed mouth, as though trying but failing to muster a proper smile.

'Are you ready, Dan?' she asks in her Irish twang.

I nod, but I'm not sure if I *am* ready. I don't know what she's written on the pages in her hands, but I'm certain it will break her heart to read the words aloud. She's trembling ever so slightly as she holds the pages up in front of her face, the way someone does when they're practising a speech.

'It seems so long ago,' she reads, her voice crumbling. 'But it's still so fresh in my mind. I remember so many moments, just like they happened yesterday. I still feel so guilty … and I still ask myself, even now, how could I give my baby away?'

She clasps her mouth shut, pressing her lips together so firmly they turn white. Her eyes are closed, her face scrunched up, like she's trying to hold it all in. But she can't. Tears build behind her thick rectangular glasses, rolling down her face and sprinkling the pages that she'd poured her soul onto. I feel a stabbing at my chest – it physically hurts to see her this way.

'I'm sorry, Dan,' she says.

I place a hand on her shoulder. 'You don't have *anything* to be sorry about. Let's stop. You don't have to read any more.'

'No,' she says, as she wipes the tears from behind her glasses. 'I need to. It's part of my healing.' She takes a few deep breaths and picks up the papers, holding them in front of her face once more in readiness to read on.

This is my mother, Bridget Donnelly, the woman who raised me. And she did so entirely as a single mother after she separated from my dad when I was just five years old. Mum features in so many of my memories, it's hard to pick which ones I should recount when describing her. I guess it's fitting to start with one of my earliest memories, during which she saves my life.

I'm four years old. Mum, my older brother, Sean, my sister, Katy, and I are at the local market. I keep begging Mum for a hotdog after we see an old Italian man selling them. 'Please, Mum. Please, Mum! Mum! Mum! Hotdog! Please!' I won't shut up. I've been at it the entire time we've been here. But she keeps telling me, 'No, Dan. It's bad for ye. I'll get ye a piece of fruit instead.' I persist with my begging, even as we're heading towards the exit gates to go home. 'Please, Mum. I want a hotdog! Pleeeeeeeease!' My persistence pays off. She finally, yet reluctantly, gives in and buys me one. While to most people the humble hotdog is the epitome of dodgy street food, to four-year-old me it's the height of culinary deliciousness.

With my brother, sister, and me fastened into our seats in the car, Mum finally hands me the precious hotdog I've been yearning for. I'm so excited that I'm telling everyone in the car all about my delicious score – so excited, in fact, that I forget to *stop* talking as I bite into the bun. Suddenly, I go quiet (for the first time all day). Mum, who's had to listen to my ramblings for hours, turns around in the driver's seat, alarmed by the silence.

Katy screams. 'He's turning blue!' she yells, her eyes wide with horror.

A big chunk of undercooked hotdog is lodged in my throat, cutting off my breath. I feel a build-up of pressure in my head that feels like it's going to pop it just like my balloon did earlier. My vision darkens around the edges as I try to draw breath. But nothing comes. The darkness closes in until I can barely see at all. I can just make out the image of Mum as she appears in front of my face. She's wide-eyed, focused and determined, but not visibly frightened. She opens my mouth with one hand and reaches into it with the other. Her fingers are at the back of my throat. In one swift move, she yanks them out again, the mushed-up bit of hotdog in her fingers. I can instantly breathe again. My lungs fill up with sweet oxygen as my vision resumes to full clarity.

'Are you alright, Danny?' Mum asks.

I say nothing. I just sit there, shaking.

'Look at me,' Mum says. 'You're okay now. Jesus! You gave me an almighty scare. That's why you don't talk while you're eating. Okay?'

I nod. And I don't say a word for the entire car trip home. All thirty minutes of it (a new world record in continual silence for four-year-old me). Mum keeps looking back in my direction through the rear-view mirror.

'Are you alright, Danny?' she keeps asking throughout the entire journey home.

I never talk while eating again.

A year or so later, before I'm old enough to go to primary school, Mum and I are waiting at the bus stop for my brother and sister to arrive for the afternoon pick-up. The big orange bus pulls around the corner, spewing a thick black cloud of fumes in its wake before it comes to a stop in front of us. The doors screech open, giving way to the cackling of schoolchildren as they pile off the bus. My brother, Sean, who's nine (four years older than me) is one of the last kids to emerge through the doors. He looks concerned. Katy is not with him. In fact, she's not on the bus at all.

'Where's Katy?' Mum asks, a shrill panic in her voice.

'The driver kicked her off,' Sean says softly.

'He *what*?' Mum says. 'Where?'

'Just around the corner,' Sean says, looking at the ground.

'Stay here,' Mum says to Sean and me as she storms off down the street and around the corner. She appears a few minutes later, walking briskly, my sister at her side. Katy, who's a year older than Sean, is bawling her eyes out, her red cheeks drenched with tears. Mum is marching towards us like a boxer entering the arena ahead of a title fight. Her eyes are narrowed, teeth gritted, and jaw clenched. They join us back at the bus stop. Mum leaves my sobbing sister with us and then marches towards the bus. She knocks on the glass doors repeatedly until the fat middle-aged man behind the wheel opens it.

'Get out here and talk to me,' Mum yells at the driver.

The fat bus driver waddles down the steps and faces my

mother. Even with a hunched back, he's still a foot taller than her and twice as wide.

'What the *hell* do you think you're doing kicking a young girl off the bus?' Mum says through gritted teeth.

'She pressed the bell too early,' the bus driver says casually.

'Jesus, Mary, and Joseph! You're havin' me on! Firstly, she just told me she *didn't* press the bell at all. And secondly, even if she did, you don't kick her off the bloody bus for it.'

'Hey, lady,' the bus driver says, putting his hands up. 'I'm sick of these kids pressing the bloody bell a hundred times before we get to the stop. They do it every day. They only need to press it *once*. Not a hundred times! So, I made her walk the last few hundred metres. Teach her a lesson. Sends a warning to the other kids not to do it as well!'

'You listen to me,' Mum says, moving in closer to the driver and pointing her finger in his face. 'You can shove your lesson up your arse. If you ever do that again, I'll be teaching *you* a lesson.'

The bus driver slowly backs away from Mum. 'Alright,' he says, putting his hands up again, accepting defeat. 'I'm sorry. I won't do it again.'

'No, you won't,' Mum says, thrusting her index finger in his face again. 'And if you do ... by God, you won't be driving this bus again. I'll make sure of it. You hear me?'

The driver nods and backs away, unable to hide the fear in his eyes.

Another memory of my mother that will always stick with me still makes me cringe, even after almost twenty years.

I'm ten years old. My grade five class is at a whole school Mass on a Wednesday morning, which we're forced to attend every few weeks or so at my Catholic primary school. Some parents and oldies from the local parish are also there. I'm sitting with my classmates towards the front of the church, trying not to fall asleep as the old priest dribbles on about ... God knows what. After communion, the priest says in his croaky monotone, 'Now for something different. I want to ask you ... any of you ... to come forward and say a prayer. It can be anything you want. Doesn't matter how big or small it is. As long as it's something you're happy to share with the *entire* school community. Come on now ... don't be shy.'

Silence spreads through the church, which is packed with several hundred kids. Some look around inquisitively at the other pews, checking if anyone will take up the priest's offer. No one does. Of course they don't – voluntarily saying an improvised prayer in front of the *entire* school would provide ammunition for bullies for years to come.

Suddenly, the sound of footsteps can be heard coming from the back of the church. Kids eagerly turn around to see who it is. Who's brave enough, stupid enough, to say a prayer in front of the *whole* school? I join my classmates and turn my head around to find out. A fiery sensation sweeps across my face. My breath cuts out. It's Mum, shuffling slowly down the aisle towards the front altar, the eyes of the *entire* school fixed upon her. I try to sink into the wooden pew as I cast my burning face towards the floor. People are nudging me from either side. There are sniggers all around.

'That's your mum, Daniel ... ha ha ha!'

Mum joins the old priest front and centre on the altar and takes the microphone from him.

'Thank you, Father,' she says into the mic, her Irish voice echoing loudly against the stone walls and soaring ceiling of the church. 'I'd like to thank the Lord for this beautiful day. And thank you, Lord, for all the lovely children here, enjoying this wonderful Mass. May you look over them, Lord, and make all their dreams come true.'

Oh shit, no. Please, Mum, just stop. I'll never live this down. The kids will never let me forget this.

'And, Lord,' Mum continues, 'watch over the children and protect them. And not just them, Lord. Look over the wonderful teachers and parents and everyone in the parish. Guide us with your strength and wisdom.'

Please stop. I can't handle any more. The sniggers and giggles are gathering strength around me, forming a chorus of ridicule that hundreds of kids seem to be taking part in. All I want to do is run out of this bloody church and never come back to this school. I can be home-schooled. At least my brother and sister won't be able to tease me about this.

'And, Lord,' Mum says. 'Help my son Daniel.'

No. No! Don't mention my name. Please, just leave me out of it.

'Lord, help Daniel with his studies. And help him on the football field. But most importantly, help him to be a *happy little boy*.'

There's no danger of that happening now. I'll never be happy again. I'll never be anything, other than mortified.

'And, Lord, finally,' Mum says, 'bless Father Brian here. Help him to overcome his recent health troubles. Give his heart the strength it needs to keep beating. We don't want it stopping again like it did a few months back.' She pats him on the back as she says this. 'Give him strength and wisdom to look after all of us. Thank you again, Lord. God bless you *all*. Amen.'

Just when I think it's over, she spots me in the crowd and waves enthusiastically, even calling to me through the microphone.

'Oh, there ye are! Hiya, Dan! I'll see ye later after school. Have a good day. Love ya.'

She finally hands the microphone back to the old priest. But the irreparable damage to my schoolyard reputation has already been done. I'll never be more embarrassed.

Of all the memories I have of my mother in my teenage years, though, there's one that will always stick with me.

I'm sixteen years old. I'm walking home from school in the searing forty-degree heat. My acne-blotched face is covered in a thick layer of sweat. The humidity has turned my curly black hair into a blossoming afro. I arrive home, throwing my heavy schoolbag down and heading straight to the fridge. It's pretty much empty. Mum must be doing food shopping on her way home from her shift at the hospital. But there's a six-pack of beer on the middle shelf. The glow from the fridge light glistens through the golden-brown bottles and the little bubbles within them. They look so good. And I'm so parched. But the beers belong to my brother, Sean, and he'll be really pissed off if I steal them. Hmm. Maybe I'll just have one. It's so hot, and I'm so thirsty. And Sean's working away for the next week, so he might not even notice there's a beer missing by the time he gets back.

I rip a bottle from the pack and twist the lid off. I've drunk beer before, occasionally, at parties. But I've never had more than a couple at one time. I tilt my head back and pour the beer down my throat. It's so bitter, I can't help but scrunch my face up. But it's also cold and strangely refreshing. And it's what men drink after a long day at work in the heat, so why shouldn't I enjoy it? The bottle is empty within a few minutes, leaving me light-headed. But I'm feeling good. I'm buzzing with a strange newfound confidence that seems to kill any fear of consequence. May as well have another one. Why bloody not? I rip another bottle from the pack and down it, quicker than the first. This one wasn't nearly as bitter. I can drink these quicker than I can drink water.

Within half an hour, all six of the bottles are empty, the beer that was within them now within my guts. My head is spinning around, and so am I. I can't stay still. The floor seems to be swaying beneath me, as though we're in the midst of a category five earthquake. I'm utterly shitfaced.

I hear a car roll into the driveway. It must be Mum. Okay, I need to act sober otherwise she'll be furious. Deep breaths and walk straight. I'll be fine. I open the front door and walk towards the car, trying to stay upright. But I'm swaying all over the place, almost veering into the garden bed.

'Hiii, Muuuuum,' I say, attempting not to slur my words. 'Lemme ... let meee ... helllp you with the shhhhopping.'

I grab the shopping bags from the back of the car, carrying them inside, almost face-planting the floor on the way. I throw the bags down on the kitchen bench and turn around to see Mum looking at me through narrowed eyes.

'Dan,' she says in a high-pitched moan. 'You're drunk!'

'Nooo. I'm not ... I'm juuust ... I only had a coupla beeers, Muuuum.'

I clasp my hands to my mouth. A burp comes out, and with it the foul acidy taste of my stomach. I stumble to the back door and struggle with the handle for a moment, only just managing to open it in time before I hurl my guts up on the timber deck outside. I'm on my hands and knees throwing up for a solid hour. Mum is standing in the doorway behind me.

'Jesus, Mary, and Joseph!' she says. 'What's got into ye? Drinking beer after school. Carryin' on like a bloody alcoholic. You're only a child!'

'I'm sorry, Mum,' I say, spitting out my last bit of vomit.

I stumble back inside and take a shower before crashing face-first onto my mattress. Mum has placed a plastic bucket next to my bed with a towel under it. My eyes are heavy, but my head feels light, like it could float out the window at any moment beyond my control. I feel the sickness coming on again, rising up from my stomach. I half roll off the bed and spew into the bucket. But my aim's not great, and I spray the surrounding carpet and wall.

'Oh, Danny,' Mum says, standing in the doorway. 'I thought you'd have more sense than that.'

It's a long night. Every now and then I wake and throw up into the bucket. And every time I wake, I notice Mum in the doorway, looking down at me. A few times I roll onto my back before feeling two hands on my shoulders, which manoeuvre me back onto my side.

The next morning, I walk into the kitchen, hair all over the place, eyes red and droopy. My head throbs and there's still the sour taste of vomit on my tongue.

'And how are ye feeling this morning?' Mum asks before taking a sip of her tea.

'I'm alright,' I say. 'I'll still go to school today.'

'Of course you're bloody going to school,' she says. 'I wouldn't be calling in sick for you. I mean, what would I say? "Sorry, Daniel can't make it in today. He's hungover. Oh did ye not know? He's a drunkard now?"'

'I'm sorry,' I say. 'But why did you keep coming into my room last night?'

'Jesus, Danny,' she says. 'I might be annoyed at you, but I'm not going to let you choke to death in the middle of the night. I was making sure you were on your side.'

Mum eventually forgave me for my drunken afterschool antics. I even convinced her to buy a new six-pack of beer to replace the one I had drunk, hence avoiding getting in more trouble from Sean.

So, that's my mother. Well, it's a few little glimpses of my mother. But she is so much more than that to me. She's the woman who picked me up as a child when I'd fallen and hurt myself; the woman who scrounged around her purse to retrieve her final few dollars so my siblings and I could spend it; the woman who scolded us through gritted teeth for swearing or misbehaving; the woman who would stand in front of the television during raunchy scenes to cover the screen and shield our innocent eyes; the woman who did shift work as a nurse so my brother, sister, and I could attend a private school; the woman who worked until her knees and back gave out from all the years of heavy lifting. No childhood is easy. But my childhood in Perth, Western Australia, is the source of many loving and happy memories, thanks mainly to my mother. While I probably never said it as much as I should have, she is someone I've always looked up to and been inspired by.

But now, in my late twenties, as I sit at her dining table in the home where she lives alone with tepid tea sitting undrunk between us, I am not looking at the mother I know. The mother I know is kind and generous and warm and jovial and courageous and fierce and always enigmatically upbeat, despite whatever is happening in her day. But the mother I'm looking at right now, sobbing as she reads, is a broken woman.

It's been about a month since Mum first asked me to help tell her story.

'I want to write a book,' she announced over the phone one day as I was driving home from work. 'I've started writing some notes already. I'd love to read it to you first, and then maybe you can put it in your own words. It's about my time in London, just after I left Ireland as a teenager.'

I instantly knew what she was referring to – the time she had a baby out of wedlock and was forced to give her away. That was more than forty years ago now. I know it still causes Mum pain, even with the remedy of time – and decades' worth of it. But the extent of her pain is something I don't know. It's something Mum and I have never properly spoken about. In fact, I barely know anything about what happened to her in London all those years ago. But now that we are here, sitting at her kitchen table and about to delve into the depths of her painful and secret past, I'm just not sure I'm prepared for what I'll learn.

I tell stories for a living. Mostly, they're stories of death and destruction, through which I've encountered the inspirational and the despicable. I've sat opposite grieving mothers and fathers wailing through a seemingly unstoppable flow of tears as they talk about their dead children. I've been to car crash scenes where body parts of someone who was a living, breathing person just moments earlier are scattered across the road for all to see. I've sat in court, listening to a man in his seventies stuttering through his description of a childhood in which he was raped and tormented by priests who were supposed to be looking after him. I've watched on as the bodies of drug smugglers, still warm from their final gasps of life, begin their journey home just moments after being shot dead by a firing squad. I've come face-to-face with a man who used his thirteen-year-old daughter as a sex slave in a paedophile ring. And through it all, through every single story I cover, I feel *something*. For I am a human being first, a storyteller second. No matter what attempt I make along the way to desensitise and distance myself from the misery of it all, my most basic human instinct, to *feel*, always emerges as something that cannot be suppressed. And now more than ever, as I begin to tell Mum's story, a story she's kept secret for so long, I know I will feel her pain as though it is my own.

'I still cry,' Mum reads on, as we sit at her table. The warm blueness in her eyes, which are so similar to my own, are now surrounded by blotches of red. 'I sometimes feel like I'm back there, in London, with her growing inside me. And it all starts to come out. The fear, the uncertainty, the pride ... the shame. Oh Lord, *of course* the shame ... it all comes back.' Her voice cuts out. Her eyes are watery again. It must be blurry to read through such teary eyes, especially when the writing is so messy. I want her to stop. I can't bear to see her like this any longer.

'I *still* feel so ashamed,' she says, dropping her head and sobbing again.

'Mum, you have nothing to be ashamed of,' I say. 'You hear me? Nothing.'

I take the crinkled papers that are blotched with teardrops and place them on the table in between the now cold cups of tea.

'Let's just leave it there for today,' I say.

'No,' she says. 'I need to, Dan.'

'Okay. But listen to me, Mum. You have *nothing* to be ashamed of.'

I know it's true. Sure, I haven't heard the full story yet. But I know Mum, and I know she would never do anything that is worthy of shame. Whatever happened in London all those years ago was forced upon her. I'm sure of it. Despite the obvious bias of sharing the same genes, I'm certain that everything about Mum is intrinsically good.

We sit in silence for a moment, with just the humming of the fridge's motor filling the room.

'I need to do this for the other mothers,' she says, as though determination has suddenly surged within her. 'The way we were treated ... it wasn't right.'

I'm divided. As a son, I'm hesitant. I don't want to see her like this again – with her tear-filled, red-stained eyes, her trembling hands, her quivering voice, and head bowed towards the floor, unable to even look at me. Whatever good comes from speaking out, it surely can't justify seeing her like this. But as a writer, I know we need to keep going. I know I need to dig deeper, to uncover every little detail from her buried memories that will allow us to properly tell her story, however painful it may be.

Mum lifts her head, wiping her eyes again from beneath her spectacles. She smiles at me. This time it's a proper smile – the corners of her mouth curve upwards, creating little ripples in her cheeks.

'It's okay, Danny. I'm stronger now than I was back then. I *need* to do this. For the other mothers.'

She picks up the papers again and scans her finger over the page, clearing her throat.

'Where was I?' she says, her voice much stronger than it was before. 'Oh yes. London, where it all began ...'

PAST

CHAPTER TWO

YOUNG LOVE

London, 1968

Bridget Reilly, fresh-faced and just eighteen years old, stood alongside half a dozen other young trainee nurses in the room at St Ann's General Hospital. Their tutor, Mr Grace, the nursing supervisor, was at the bedside of an elderly male patient. The young nurses listened intently as their eloquently spoken and immaculately groomed tutor addressed them.

'Now, girls,' Mr Grace said. 'Bathing the patients is just as important as anything else you do in your day. That includes dispensing medication, attending to wounds, writing reports, basically *anything* ... Am I clear? You need to take *time* and *care*. Treat the patient like you would want your own mother or father to be treated.'

Mr Grace spoke in a soft yet authoritative voice and had a very subtle lisp. One of the girls had once suggested he spoke this way because he was a homosexual. But Bridget couldn't understand how those two things could be linked.

'Nurse Edmonds!' Mr Grace said. 'Take the cloth and wipe down Mr Jones's left arm.'

The young student nurse did as she was told, wiping the old man's liver-spotted arm, the skin so loose it looked like a half-empty hessian bag.

'Miss O'Callaghan,' Mr Grace went on. 'You're next. Do the same thing to Mr Jones's right arm.'

Part by part, each of the girls washed down the incapacitated old man in the hospital bed. Mr Jones lay back, grinning, apparently unfazed by the host of young nurses bathing him like he'd never been bathed before. Bridget's face started to burn. It was a familiar sizzling sensation that struck whenever redness tinged her cheeks. She'd always been prone to blushing easily. But she'd done a *lot* of it, even by her standards, during the past year as she adjusted to life in the big city.

Mr Jones had now been cleaned from top to bottom – from his densely wrinkled face and neck, his arms, chest and back (which were covered in a forest of grey curly hairs), down to his heavily bruised legs and bloated feet. But there was still *one* part that hadn't been cleaned. And Bridget was the only nurse who hadn't yet been tasked with bathing duties. The sizzling sensation in her cheeks spread like wildfire throughout the rest of her face. *Oh God no*, she thought. *I'm going to have to wash his willy!* She had never even seen anyone naked before this moment, so she couldn't bear to look at the wrinkly bits of the partially nude old man in the hospital bed. This was not what she imagined being a nurse in London would be like.

The other young nurses, who had already fulfilled their bathing duties, clasped their hands to their mouths, struggling to contain their laughter, as Bridget's impending torture closed in. The room went silent, and she felt the eyes of all the girls fall upon her. Mr Grace's gaze was also directed at her, like a teacher waiting for a student to answer a simple question in class. Mr Jones, the elderly patient, had his hands behind his head, wearing a toothy grin (despite missing most of his teeth), in readiness for the highly anticipated final part of his bath. Bridget dropped her head towards the floor, the burning in her face still growing, the quietness lingering. The time to carry out her torturous task had arrived.

Mr Grace finally broke the silence as he turned back to the old patient. 'Mr Jones,' he said, 'would you mind washing your own privates and spare Nurse Reilly of the task? Many thanks!'

The girls giggled uncontrollably. Bridget would have laughed with them. But she was too relieved to laugh. By this stage in her training, she'd seen dead bodies, been yelled at more times than she cared to remember, and come across about every infectious disease one could imagine. But it was this, her introduction to bed baths, that almost tipped her over the edge of sanity.

Bridget had been living in London for one year. But she still felt strange calling it home. For the first seventeen years of her life, the only home she'd known was Belmullet – a tiny town on the west coast of Ireland, where she'd grown up in a little cottage on a small farm. She was the youngest of six children and the last to leave home. She probably would have been happy to stay in Belmullet her entire life, had her mammy not insisted she move to London to become a nurse. So, like any well-behaved Irish Catholic daughter, Bridget did as she was told and moved from her sleepy village to a city of millions. At first, she was alone and terrified in London. But those fears were quickly overcome by the excitement of meeting new people, making a living (yet barely having a penny to her name), and exploring the apparently never-ending sights and attractions of London.

She made so many new friends during her first year in the big smoke. Her closest friends were Mary, Teresa, and Brenda. They were also young nurses from out of town. Like Bridget, Mary and Teresa were from Ireland. Brenda was from Trinidad – a country Bridget had never heard of until they'd met. The four girls seemed to become best friends straight away, much like children do during their first days of school. There were no limits to their friendship. Whether they were laughing about the latest pranks they'd played on each other or spilling their innermost thoughts and feelings during teary conversations, they were *always* there for each other.

Bridget's first year in London was also one of yearning for home. She spent many long nights crammed in her tiny dorm room, thinking of her farm and family cottage in Belmullet, and, of course, her mammy and daddy, who were now all alone in that home. The bouts of homesickness dropped off by the end of her first year. But she was still prone to the occasional case of it, usually after a bad day on the hospital wards.

It was a year of learning. Bridget had been thrust into the pressure cooker of St Ann's General Hospital, where she learnt her trade as a nurse. She, and the other young nurses, learnt by doing – on the chaotic wards of the hospital, instead of in the safety and comfort of a classroom. There was no overriding pass or fail in her studies, just human life, which sometimes edged a little too close to the brink of her control.

It was a year of discovery. She'd come to the big city knowing very little about the world outside Belmullet (where practically everyone was a Catholic and had skin as white as snow). London opened Bridget's eyes to other cultures – people who believed in a different god, or gods, or sometimes no god at all. She couldn't help but stare when she saw people with dark skin for the first time. She was fascinated by them and often had to fight the urge to go up to them and ask all about their background. She learnt so much about the world during that first year, especially from the other nurses who had come from different parts of Europe and Africa. But still there was so much to be learnt. And she was eager.

Eighteen was a year of so many things for Bridget. But it wasn't until her second year in London that her life *really* changed.

At nineteen years of age, she still had never loved a boy. She'd always loved her mammy and her daddy, her brothers and sister, her animals, her home town, but never a boy. The thought of falling in love with a boy had never really entered her mind. That was until one Saturday night in London.

Saturday nights were the best time of the week for the young nurses at St Ann's. In the lead up to them, the young women spent almost every waking hour working on the wards of the hospital: walking from room to room; giving bed baths to elderly patients; trying not to breathe in when they looked after men and women with highly infectious diseases; getting yelled at by their tutors for not addressing someone in the proper manner (Yes, sir. Yes, ma'am); clearing away and cleaning soiled bedpans; helplessly watching old pensioners take their final breaths; wheeling cold, stiff corpses to the morgue; nervously adding up the dosage of drugs they'd just given to their patients out of fear they'd accidentally killed them – the chaos of working in the hospital never stopped. But all of that was always forgotten on Saturday nights. Groups of girls would gather in the dorm rooms, where they'd laugh and gossip and share make-up and clothes as they prettied themselves up for a night on the town. And then the fun really started. The girls would cram into London's pulsating discos and clubs and dance into the wee hours. Some would spend their precious few pounds on drinking. Not Bridget, though. She had no interest in wasting any of the little money she had on alcohol. She'd only ever had one *proper* drink during a night out, and it hadn't gone down too well.

'Jesus, Mary, and Joseph! What was that?' she'd said as she spat out the foul-tasting concoction one of the girls had just handed to her. 'How can ya drink that? It's disgusting!'

The girls around her giggled, then took the drink from her hand.

She had no interest in giving alcohol another chance after that. She didn't need to get drunk to have a good time with her friends. Because that's essentially all Saturday nights were about – fun with friends. Or as the Irish girls called it – 'good craic!'

This particular Saturday night, when Bridget's nineteen-year-old life changed forever, started with a knock at her dorm room door. She opened it to find Colette, a young nurse she'd become friends with over the past year. Colette was a short blonde woman in her early twenties and was a little bit lumpy around the waist. Like Bridget, she was also from Ireland and had moved to London a few years earlier to become a nurse. Tonight, she was going out on the town with her boyfriend. But one of his friends would be with him, so Colette had asked Bridget to come along and keep her company. And even up the gender balance of the group, so to speak.

'You're ready, Bridget?' Colette said impatiently. 'They should be out the front any minute.'

Colette led the way out of the dorm room towards the front of the hospital. The nurses' accommodation was within the grounds of St Ann's. It came in handy after a long shift, when all Bridget wanted to do was crash face-first into her bed. A high wall of dreary grey bricks surrounded the outside of the precinct. It was a fairly dull sight – void of any colour, apart from the occasional patch of moss on the outside walls.

Colette was walking quickly, a few feet ahead of Bridget, apparently in a hurry to jump into her boyfriend's arms. 'There he is,' she said, leading the way across the street.

A rusty white sedan was parked on the other side of the road. Two young men were sitting in it. The man on the passenger's side opened his door and wrapped his arms around Colette, pulling her in for a kiss, like a long-lost couple reuniting after years apart. His name was Jamal – a short, dark-skinned man who seemed to always have a cheeky grin on his face. He was well below six feet and shorter than Bridget but still tall enough to stand above Colette. Jamal was neatly dressed in a plain white shirt, which was tucked into his crisp black trousers. The man in the driver's seat also got out of the car to greet them. Like Jamal, this young man had brown skin. He was much taller than Jamal, but quite skinny. His curly jet-black hair was clumsily parted to one side. He was wearing a brown suit, the trousers about an inch too small for him, revealing his pulled-up white socks. The young man hastily straightened his suit out, his eyes darting from Colette to Bridget. He nervously rubbed his hands together before holding one out to Bridget.

'Nice to meet you,' he quietly mumbled in a foreign accent, which Bridget assumed was Indian. 'I'm Amir.'

She held out her hand and shook his. His grip was soft and warm, his palms slightly sweaty. She immediately noticed his big brown eyes, which looked into hers for a moment. But then they quickly scurried away towards the ground as he let go of her grip.

'Hello, I'm Bridget—' she finally replied.

'Yes, yes,' Colette interrupted. 'Well, now that you two have met, let's get in the car. It's feckin' freezin' out here.'

Colette and Bridget piled into the back seats of the car, the two boys in the front, before they set off through London's busy streets.

'This disco is meant to be great,' Colette said as she checked her reflection in the window and adjusted her hair. 'Some of the girls went there the other week. Said 'twas great craic!'

Jamal laughed and turned around from the front seat to face Colette. 'Your Irish words ... *crack* ... it makes me laugh,' he said.

'He's always laughin' at me,' Colette said, winking at Bridget. 'That's why I brought you with me. To look after me.'

Bridget smiled but said nothing. She suddenly noticed Amir's big brown eyes again, this time in the rear-view mirror as he glanced in her direction. But it was only a fleeting look, and he quickly turned his attention back towards the road in front of them. Colette and Jamal did all the talking as the car slowly made its way through a stream of London traffic towards the West End. Every now and then, Bridget noticed Amir's eyes in the mirror. She could feel her cheeks burning, so she was glad the street lights weren't bright enough to shine into the car and reveal the extent of her blushing.

They parked up and negotiated their way through the masses of people on the footpaths of Oxford Street. Colette and Jamal walked ahead, hand in hand. Bridget and Amir followed just behind them, not saying anything at all. Amir had his hands in his pockets, his head hunched towards the ground. Bridget was too nervous to look in his direction, so she stared ahead towards Colette and Jamal. They were both laughing. Jamal would occasionally turn to Colette and peck her on the cheek and she'd turn back to him and wrap her arm around his waist. Colette was *different* around Jamal. It was as though nothing else, or no one else, existed when he was in her presence.

When they finally got into the nightclub, the wooden floor was vibrating to the beats of music blaring through massive speakers on the walls. A huge disco ball hung from the ceiling, a sea of colour under it. And in among the flashing lights of yellow, blue, white, and red were young men and women enthusiastically dancing. Not dancing like they did in Ireland. This was a different level of dancing, with flailing arms and spinning and lifting and grinding and unashamed public canoodling. Bridget had only ever seen dancing like this in the movies – until she'd moved to London.

Amir turned to Bridget, Colette, and Jamal and said something – the first thing he'd said since he introduced himself earlier. But it was too loud for Bridget to make out the words. All she could hear were the reverberations of the music. Amir leaned in close, his aftershave hitting her nostrils as he spoke in her ear.

'I'm going to get everyone a drink at the bar,' he said. 'What would you like, Bridget?'

'Oh, that's lovely of ye,' she said. 'Arr ... not alcohol, please. Terrible stuff. Lemonade would be grand. Thanks!'

Amir returned a few minutes later with four drinks, which he'd paid for with his own money. Colette and Jamal took their hands off each other for a moment so they could take their glasses. All four of them then found a spot on the packed dance floor, where they could be within arm's reach of each other without being separated by other dancers invading their space. And there on the vibrating floor, under the flashing lights and glitter of the disco ball, among energetic crowds of revellers, the four of them danced the night away. People came and went around them, but the four of them never swayed from each other's presence, apart from the many times Amir went to the bar to generously buy drinks for them all. They danced to the likes of The Beatles, Tom Jones, Elvis Presley, and Cliff Richards. Colette and Jamal couldn't take their hands off each other. They seemed infatuated, both of them like a child not wanting to stray too far from the safe embrace of a parent – they just didn't let each other go. None of them could talk above the blaring beats coming from the speakers. Not that Bridget and Amir would have been talking. She had definitely come out of her shell in the past year, but she was still prone to a regular case of blushing, especially when in the presence of a boy she'd only just met – particularly one who was throwing frequent sideways glances at her.

And the night ended with one of those glances. Colette and Jamal were leaning on the rusty white car outside St Ann's, giving each other a passionate goodnight kiss. Amir took hold of Bridget's right hand with both of his. His big brown eyes looked into hers as though there was a tunnel between them and nothing else in the world outside of it.

'It was very nice to meet you,' Amir said.

'You too,' Bridget said softly. She was thankful she hadn't had to say much to Amir all night because of the deafening music in the club. But right now, in the late-night quiet of the street in front of the hospital, it was a lot harder to hide her nervousness. Amir let go of her hand and got back into the car. And then, as she walked back towards the front gates of the hospital with Colette, she turned back and saw Amir glancing at her, like he had been doing all night. He appeared to notice she was looking back at him, so he quickly looked away. Bridget's chest tightened. Of all the people she'd met during her time in London, she'd never felt like this.

In the weeks that followed, Bridget and Colette went out on the town with Amir and Jamal countless times. Sometimes the other nurses from St Ann's joined them and they'd party in big groups. But even when they were in those big groups, cramming themselves into overflowing clubs, Bridget started to feel as though there were only two people in the room. Whenever she saw Amir, her heart would flutter, her mouth would go dry, and her hands would get clammy. But after a few weeks, that feeling began to linger, even when Amir wasn't around. All it would take was a thought of him or a mention of his name for the sensation to hit. She'd been struck with nerves many times before. But this was different. It was an inexplicable tightening in her chest. It was a tingling throughout her entire body that came without warning. It was an unshakeable smile on her face that she only realised was there when she saw her reflection or if someone remarked on how happy she looked. Whatever was happening to her, it was getting stronger with each passing day. She felt as though she were falling further and further into the unknown.

About two months after their first Saturday night out together, Amir finally asked Bridget the question she'd been waiting for.

'So, would you ... like to be ... my girlfriend?' he asked softly at the front of the hospital after a night on the town.

Bridget's cheeks instantly burned, and she knew they would have been a tomato shade of red. 'I would love to be ... I would love to ... go out with ye .... be your ... grand ... oh yes, I'd love to be your ...'

'Girlfriend,' Amir interjected.

'Yes,' she replied, her lips growing into a large grin.

Amir smiled back at her. He reached out and took her hands into his, leaned forward and kissed her. Bridget and Amir looked so different next to each other, entwined in each other's grip. Her skin was pale as snow, apart from little flecks of light brown freckles, which were splattered on her nose, under her eyes, and down her arms. His skin was brown, with hair covering his head and arms that matched a pitch-black night sky. Bridget had heard many people say that a man and woman with different coloured skin should not be together, that it's an *unnatural pairing*. But to her, particularly in this moment, it didn't matter. Amir's big brown eyes stared into Bridget's piercing blue ones. Her heart fluttered, as it had been doing for the past few months. And she felt like that fluttering feeling would never stop.

And so it began. Life with Amir was blissfully perfect. Like Bridget, he didn't have much money. He worked in a factory that made leather handbags. Within a few weeks, he'd given her more handbags than she thought she'd need in her entire life. He also spent every last penny on her. Every week he'd lavish her with gifts. She'd arrive for work at the hospital to find a delivery of red roses or a big bunch of daisies. And it would always come with a card that said something like 'For my one and only. Love Amir,' or 'A beautiful rose for my beautiful Irish rose.' Amir would also arrive at St Ann's on Friday and Saturday nights with golden bracelets and necklaces, which Bridget would proudly wear as they went out to restaurants around London. Eating at restaurants was an entirely new experience for her. She'd grown up on fresh fruit and vegetables from the yard, fish from the Atlantic, and recently slaughtered chicken and beef from the fields. But she'd never tried curry or any of the tongue-tingling spices of the subcontinent that Amir ate every day. One night, Amir took her to a little Indian restaurant on the outskirts of London to give her a first taste of his homeland.

'I'll order you the mild,' he said, placing his hand on hers in a reassuring way.

'Ah, that'd be grand,' she replied. 'I've heard about what happens when the hot ones come out the arse end.'

She regretted her bluntness almost as instantly as she'd said it. But Amir didn't look disgusted, as she feared he would. He shook with laughter at her, his pearly white teeth gleaming.

Another night, during dinner at an Irish pub, Bridget casually spoke about her desire to go to a lights festival in Liverpool. She'd heard from one of the young nurses, who was from Liverpool, that it was a sight to behold. Several weeks later, Amir surprised her with a trip there, which he had extensively planned. The festival was as spectacular as she'd been told. A kaleidoscope of colourful lights, lanterns, and fireworks lit up the night sky. When Bridget wasn't looking up at the spectacle above, she was glancing over at Amir and thinking *how lucky am I?*

Amir had been living in London for five years before they met. Like Bridget, he had come from another country with the hopes and dreams that only this city could fulfil. But their backgrounds couldn't have been more different. He had grown up among the chaotic colour of Bombay, India. Bridget didn't know much about India. But she soon learnt that certain things were done very differently in India, none more so than marriage. Amir told her all about it one Saturday afternoon as they walked through Hyde Park.

'My family …' he said. 'There are things I can't tell them because they will not understand.'

'God help us,' Bridget said. 'Don't you be worrying about that right now. Ye know it's the same with my family.'

'It's not just about you and me,' he replied. 'Things are very different in my culture. You see ... my mother and father have found *someone* for me in Bombay.'

'Christ,' Bridget said softly.

Amir raised his eyebrows at her reaction.

'No, I'm not sayin' it's Christ they found for ya,' she said. 'Just saying ... *Christ* ... that's an odd thing for parents to be doing.'

'There is a woman they want me to marry,' Amir said. 'Both our families have agreed.'

She stopped walking, lost for words.

'I have no choice in the matter,' Amir continued. 'They have decided we are to marry ... and whatever *I* think about it means nothing.'

'Lord above,' Bridget said. 'Who is this woman?'

'It doesn't matter. My parents can disown me. They can be ashamed of me for the rest of their lives. But I'm never going back there and marrying her ... I love *you*.'

She looked into his big brown eyes, which appeared to have a teary glisten in them, and she believed every word he was saying.

Dating was entirely new to Bridget. She had boys as friends growing up in Belmullet. But she never dated anyone. As for sex, well, she didn't have the slightest understanding or notion of sex until she was thirteen years old. Her older cousin, Kelly, who was fifteen, was visiting Belmullet when she explained it.

'You know how babies are made, right?' Kelly had asked as they walked in the fields along the coast.

'Course I do,' Bridget replied confidently.

'How then?'

Bridget stopped and thought for a moment before answering. 'Well. They come in with the tide, don't they?'

Kelly smirked, holding her hands to her mouth. 'You're not serious?'

'I am!' Bridget barked back. 'Didn't your mammy and daddy tell you that when you were a wee girl? Babies come in with the tide of the sea.'

'And how does the baby swim in the sea?' Kelly asked, still grinning.

'It's not swimming. It's floatin' in a box. That's how the Lord tells the angels to deliver the little ones.'

'In a box?' Kelly went on. 'And have you ever *seen* one of these floatin' boxes comin' in with the tide?'

'Well, no,' Bridget answered. 'But I'm always on the lookout when I'm down by the sea. You know, in case one comes in and needs to be picked up.'

Kelly's whole body shook as she cracked up. 'Jaysus! You're feckin' jokin'! I'm sorry, Bridget, but that's *not* how it happens.'

'How then?' Bridget asked.

Kelly took a moment to consider her response. 'You know when the cow is acting up?' she said. 'And then your daddy takes her down to the Pattersons' yard? And then they put the cow in the pen with the bull?'

'Yeah,' Bridget responded, unaware of the relevance of her question.

'And then the bull mounts the cow. Well ... what happens a few months after that? A little calf comes along.'

Bridget's eyes narrowed as she thought about this. But still, the relevance didn't dawn on her.

'The bull and the cow were having *sex*!' Kelly continued. 'The bull was putting its willy in the cow's fanny.'

Bridget fell to the ground laughing. *What a strange thing to make up*, she thought. 'You're daft!' she said when she finally stopped chuckling. 'Why would Mammy and Daddy tell me babies come in with the tide then?'

'Because,' Kelly said, 'your mammy and daddy don't want ye to know that ye were made the same way the cow and bull made the calf.'

That was the first time anyone had explained sex to Bridget. But even six years later, as a nineteen-year-old in London with her first boyfriend, she barely knew anything about sex. Despite her cluelessness, not long after she'd started dating Amir, it happened. And with it came an inevitable bout of Irish Catholic guilt.

Bridget and Amir dated for a year. She was so happy in their early days together. He made her laugh. And when she wasn't laughing, she was smiling. She couldn't imagine ever not being completely and utterly in love with him. But she was young and naïve and when things changed between them, they changed quickly.

A day wouldn't go past without Amir calling the nurses' home to speak to her. 'Hello, I want to speak to Bridget,' he'd say. And if she wasn't there he'd ask, 'Well, where is she? What is she doing? Who is she seeing? How long has she been gone? Tell her to call Amir.'

When Bridget *did* talk to him, he'd ask even more questions. 'What did you do today? Who did you see? What are their names? What's that noise in the background? Who's there with you? What are you doing after this? When can I see you next?'

At first, Bridget didn't really mind the phone calls and barrage of questions that came with them. But as the months passed they became more frequent, while Amir's tone darkened.

It was just after eight o'clock on a Monday evening when Amir made his daily call to the nurses' home.

'Hello, I want to speak to Bridget,' he said.

'Oh, hiya,' the young nurse answered. 'Wait a wee minute and I'll go find out where she is.'

The young nurse returned to the phone a few minutes later. 'Sorry, she's not here.'

There was a brief moment of silence over the phone before Amir spoke again. 'Where is she?' he asked.

'Oh, not far away. Just at the pub. You know, the Irish one around the corner. There's a band on tonight apparently.'

'Okay, thank you,' Amir said, hanging up.

Bridget was with her work friend Mary at the pub, where they'd been enjoying a night of toe-tapping sounds of the fiddle and flute and lyrics from their homeland. London's Irish pubs provided a small taste of the craic that Bridget and her friends missed so much, so they'd occasionally drop in after a long shift at the hospital.

As Bridget was leaving the pub with Mary at the end of the night, she noticed a white car parked on the other side of the road. A dark figure was in the front seat. Only the whites of his eyes were visible. *It's Amir.* She was sure he'd be furious – he hated when she did things without him or without telling him.

Bridget and Mary turned right and walked along the footpath, back towards St Ann's General Hospital. The drone of a car turning on sounded behind them. Bridget was starting to panic. *What is he going to do?*

Mary must have also noticed Amir. 'What's he doing here?' she asked.

'Just keep walkin',' Bridget said.

The white glow of the headlights shone on them from behind, casting giant shadows of both girls onto the street ahead. Bridget's heart was now thumping furiously. She'd been intimidated when relentlessly questioned by Amir during phone calls in the past, but she'd never been frightened like this – terrified of the man she was supposed to be in love with. It felt as though Amir's eyes were piercing into the back of her head. They walked for several hundred feet with the car's motor buzzing behind them like a persistent mosquito, while the headlights followed them like they were prison escapees moving through a jail yard. Finally, after a few minutes, the car screeched up beside them, coming to a stop. The window rolled down and Amir leaned out, calling to them.

'Bridget,' he said. 'Get in. I'm driving you home.'

Bridget and Mary both jumped in the car, Bridget in the front, Mary in the back. Not a word was spoken during the five-minute drive back to St Ann's. Bridget and Mary just stared out the window while Amir kept his eyes on the road and breathed heavily. He pulled up at the hospital, then turned back to Mary.

'Goodnight,' he said.

Mary looked at Bridget for a moment, as though checking she was okay, then she got out of the car. Bridget went to follow, opening the front passenger's door, but Amir turned and grabbed her arm.

'You're not going anywhere,' he said. 'I need to talk to you.'

His voice was quiet but stern, and his teeth clenched as he spoke. Bridget thought about freeing her arm, jumping out of the car and running to safety. But she decided against it. Amir put his foot down and the car abruptly sped off, up the street. He was staring ahead, his nostrils flaring, his breath rapid. The car veered quickly around a bend, almost going onto the wrong side of the road. The engine revved boisterously as the car picked up speed. All the while, not a word was spoken between them. Bridget was no longer looking out the window; she focused ahead at the blur of streetlights and buildings they were whizzing past.

'Jesus, Amir! Slow down,' she yelled.

The roar of the engine grew louder as Amir put his foot down even further. She closed her eyes and clenched her fingers around the firm cushion of the seat, holding on for dear life. *Lord help us. We're going to die.* Then, suddenly, the roar of the engine died down to a dull drone. She could feel the car slowing down, so she opened her eyes and caught a glimpse of Amir. He had both hands on the wheel, still staring blankly ahead, his jaw clenched firmly, his cheek muscles twitching. He pulled the car over, turned the ignition off, and spoke to her.

'Why didn't you tell me you were going out tonight?' he demanded. 'I had no idea where you were.'

'Jesus, Amir,' she said. 'I was just with a friend.'

Amir shook his head. 'Why would you do that? I've told you I don't want you going out without me. I've *told* you that.'

'We were just listening to music. That's all.'

Amir looked away. 'I don't understand why you would do something like this to me. I'm your boyfriend. You shouldn't keep secrets from me.'

'Amir,' Bridget replied. 'I wasn't keeping *secrets* from ya. I was just with my friend ... that's all.'

'But why?' Amir asked, his eyes narrowing. 'A girlfriend should not act like this. She should be loyal to the man who loves her and tell him everything she is doing. If you are to be my wife one day, you can't continue to act like this.'

Bridget tried to think of what words she could spit out to make this right in his eyes. But there were none that came to mind. Instead of the heart-fluttering affection she once had for him, her heart was now beating rapidly for all the wrong reasons. Amir buried his face in his hands and exhaled. For the first time in their relationship, she felt like she had become one of Amir's possessions. And she knew at that moment she needed to get out. Not just out of the car, but also out of the emotional hold he had on her.

Several days later, Bridget met up with Amir at the front gates of the hospital. She'd planned to end things once and for all.

'I'm sorry, Amir,' she said. 'But I can't do this any more.'

Amir pressed his lips together and shook his head with a quiet sort of rage. 'You don't want to marry me because I'm not a Catholic,' he said.

'It's not that, Amir,' she replied. 'You know that doesn't matter to me.'

'Then why haven't you told your family about me?' he asked. 'Because I'm dark?'

'Don't be daft! I haven't told them for the same reason you haven't told yours about me. They won't accept us being together. You know that. I don't give a shite about the colour of your skin or the colour of your arse or the bloody colour of anything. It's not about *that*. I just can't … keeping doing this. I'm sorry.'

Amir clenched his fists, his knuckles turning white. Bridget was scared to linger in his presence, in case he made a scene, so she turned her back and walked away into the safety of St Ann's General Hospital. And that was it. Their relationship had come to an unpleasant end a year after it first blossomed on the dance floor of a London nightclub. Bridget's first taste of young love had turned sour.

But it turned out Amir was hard to get away from. Several months later, their paths crossed again. Colette was still seeing Jamal. And so Bridget and Amir were inadvertently pulled back together through their circle of friends. It started with an innocent hello when they saw each other at a West End nightclub on a Saturday night. Then they spoke some more when Amir gave her a lift home in the early hours of the morning. Then Bridget saw Amir another night at a different club, and he asked to take her out for dinner, just to catch up. *Just an innocent catch-up,* she thought. *Why not?* Plus, Colette was very insistent. 'Just go have dinner with him,' she said. ''Twould be great to have the two of you together again. Then you two can join me and Jamal on the nights out. We've been missing ya. You're not making it easy on me as well.'

Bridget somewhat reluctantly went to dinner with Amir. Then one dinner turned into two, then three ... then the phone calls started again. Amir would ring the nurses' home every night and demand to know everything about her day. After a few months, things between them were just as they had been before they'd broken up. Bridget had been reeled back in, almost without realising it. She was annoyed at herself for giving in to his persistence, for falling into his traps. But in another way, she was just conceding – fearing she'd never be able to get him out of her life. He was too determined, too obsessed. He'd surely never let her go, not while she was still in London. And even if she did escape the city she'd grown to love, she thought he'd surely find a way to track her down and keep her within his grasp.

Bridget was now twenty years old and had lived in London for two years. And she felt like that time had well and truly taken its toll on her. She was in the midst of an unhappy relationship, homesick, overworked, and underpaid. Those are the reasons why she thought she was ill. She'd been throwing up every day before work for a week straight. The sickly churning in her guts hit like clockwork, every day at quarter to seven just before her shift started. She'd get in to work a little early and throw up in the bathroom before starting her morning rounds. But on Friday morning, she couldn't even lift herself out of bed to put her uniform on. Her mouth was full of vomit before she made it to the bathroom. While wrapped around the cold white porcelain of the toilet bowl and spitting out the acidy taste of puke, she decided to call in sick for work. She'd go and see the doctor instead, and get this dealt with properly.

Bridget sat in Dr Wilkins' office as he examined her. The old doctor took some bloods and checked out her chest and throat.

'Well, you look terrible,' he said. 'Could be the common cold. Could be just about *anything* you've picked up from any one of your patients. But we'll wait till we get the bloods back before we jump to any conclusions. For now, drink as much water as you can stomach. And ... lots of bed rest! I'll see you in a few days.'

Bridget spent the next two mornings hurling her guts up over the toilet bowl, just as she had been doing the previous week. On Monday, she returned to see Dr Wilkins, hoping she'd finally be given some antibiotics, or anything, to make her feel better. Dr Wilkins sat opposite her, reading through some notes in a manila folder. He flicked it shut and addressed her.

'Miss Reilly, we've found the problem,' he said. 'I'm sure you can think back to what you did to get yourself in this situation.'

Bridget sat in silence, frozen to her chair. Every infectious disease she'd encountered over the last few weeks were running through her head. *Tuberculosis, pneumonia, typhoid, influenza, measles, meningitis ... What deadly disease have I got?*

Dr Wilkins finally broke the deafening silence.

'Miss Reilly, you're pregnant.'

CHAPTER THREE

IT'S NOT TRUE

I*t's not true. It's not true. It's not true.*

Bridget sat in front of the television in the common area of the nurses' home, blankly staring at the TV. But she wasn't paying attention to what was on. Through her eyes, the screen was a mere flicker of blurry black-and-white movement, the sound from the speakers just muffled white noise. As they'd say in Belmullet, she was away with the fairies. This was the only TV in the building. It was a place the girls would come to relax after a long gruelling shift. It was also a popular form of free entertainment, which was welcome considering how little the nurses got paid. The common room had become Bridget's retreat from the outside world. Her friends Brenda and Teresa were sitting alongside her on the sofa, but unlike her, they were actually paying attention to the blaring television. Other girls sat in chairs around the room, their eyes glued to the screen. Some of them sat around a large table in the back corner drinking tea and casually gossiping, but not too loudly so the girls watching the TV wouldn't tell them to shut up.

Bridget was exhausted. She'd woken at dawn and spent most of the morning throwing up. She was then on her feet for the rest of the day, doing her rounds through the hospital, with barely a minute's break for a cup of tea or a sandwich. Not that she would have been able to stomach either.

'You alright, Bridget?' Teresa asked, nudging her in the side.

'Ah, I'm fine,' Bridget said. 'Just knackered.'

'You look blind drunk,' Teresa said. 'Which makes no sense when you've never had a drink in your life.'

Teresa reached out her hand and held it against Bridget's forehead. 'No fever. But it's probably worth seeing the doctor if you're still under the weather tomorrow.'

'No, I'm grand,' Bridget said. 'Just tired is all.'

Mary, Bridget's other close friend, walked into the room. 'Bridget!' she yelled. 'Phone for ya.'

She knew straight away who it was. There was no question who it was. It was just past 8 p.m. and he hadn't called yet. *I have to tell him it's over.* The thought had been bouncing around her head all day. But the prospect of actually doing it was terrifying.

'Hello,' Bridget said in a trembling voice as she picked up the phone.

'You don't sound well,' Amir said. 'What's the matter?'

Bridget paused, clenching her quivering fingers around the telephone, trying to find the words to answer him.

'Bridget, what is it?' he continued.

'I'm sorry, Amir,' she finally said.

'What are you sorry about?' Amir snapped back. 'What did you do?'

She inhaled and tried to compose herself. 'Amir, I can't see you any more. I'm sorry.'

Amir went quiet. All she could hear was the heavy rustling of his breath through the earpiece. 'Because I'm not a Catholic!' he said. 'That's it, isn't it? That shouldn't matter.'

'Oh Lord, it doesn't,' Bridget said. 'Jesus, I don't care about your religion. I ... just can't give you what you want. It'll never work.'

Amir's breath grew louder through the earpiece, before he spoke next. 'But we love each other,' he said, his voice softening.

Bridget kind of felt sorry for him. And for a fleeting moment, she felt him reeling her back in, just as he had before. *No! I have to be strong,* she told herself.

'Not any more,' she said.

'Why then?' Amir snapped back, his voice hardening again. 'Why don't you love me? I don't believe you. I need to see you. I can't live without you.' He got louder with every word he spoke.

'Jesus, Amir. No! I'm sorry.'

'I'm coming to see you,' he said. 'I'm coming to the hospital.'

'I'll never be happy with you,' she said, her voice firmer than it was before. 'I can't breathe when I'm with you. You're ... you're obsessed, Amir. That'll be it now. Don't call me again.'

She hung up. And not a moment too soon. She burst into tears as she shakily placed the phone back on the hook. She buried her trembling hands in her pockets and headed towards her dorm room. She didn't feel like going back to the common room and being around the other girls. *I need to sleep,* she thought. *Maybe when I wake up, this will all be over.*

In her dorm room, she peered out of her window at the starless night sky. She had looked up at that same sky two years earlier, in awe of how bright it was, yet dumbstruck at the absence of stars. A hazy blanket of light smothered the city, rendering the heavens different shades of dark grey. She had become used to it, but she still yearned to see the twinkle of stars, just like they did above Belmullet at night. The haze that hung over London was just another reminder that she was a long way from home.

She threw herself under the sheets and shut her eyes. Her muscles were stiff from her toes to the top of her neck. Her stomach churned, the tightness in her chest hadn't let up, and now her head throbbed as though a thousand hot needles were piercing into it. But she could deal with all of that. It was her *mind* that was too much to handle. It had been racing all day with thoughts of her sickness and, of course, Amir. And no matter how many times she gave bed baths, handed out meds, and cleaned bed pans, she couldn't find a way to distract herself. *It's not true –* she kept telling herself that as she tossed and turned on her lumpy mattress, trying to find that elusive comfortable position. It took an hour or so before sleep finally came upon her, and with it, her first moment of peace for the day.

It's not true. For weeks, Bridget forced that same thought every night as she lay in bed before drifting off to peaceful oblivion. Sleep was her only real escape from the world, a world that was closing in on her. But every morning, she'd wake with the same realisation: *Today is the same as yesterday. Nothing's changed.* As she rolled out of bed, she'd feel a lump of queasiness rising up her throat. She'd barely make it to the communal bathroom of the nurses' home before it exploded out her mouth. Once she'd retched and spat every last bit of sick and was starting to feel a bit better, it was time to get ready for work. She'd arrive on the ward fifteen minutes early. By that stage, the early morning post-spew relief had worn off. The second wave of nausea was now crashing into her. The hospital bathrooms would usually be vacant at that time, allowing her to bring up any remaining contents from her stomach, including the lining itself. If there was another woman in the bathroom, Bridget tried to hold it in and be quiet. She'd stand dead still in the cubicle, clasping her mouth shut, closing her eyes, and holding her breath to the point she'd almost pass out. But sometimes she couldn't hold it in, so she'd lay toilet paper over the water to stop the splashing sound of the vomit hitting it. When the wave of nausea passed again, she'd wipe her mouth and fix the stray hairs that had come loose from her bun. She'd then examine herself in the bathroom mirror to make sure her hat was straight, her hair neat, her gold nurse's watch properly pinned in place, her white apron and blue blouse crisp and free of any creases or stains, and her black shoes shiny, free from scuffs, and without any spots of vomit.

The young nurses were always being yelled at about their appearance. 'Straighten that hat ... Tie that hair up ... and get it cut while you're at it ... Clean those shoes ... Pull those tights up ... Get a new apron, that one's covered in blood!' Bridget didn't want to give the senior nurses or tutors any excuse to yell at her in case it drew attention to her sickness. Once she was neat and tidy, she'd have one final look in the mirror and try to curl her lips into a smile. She'd need that smile to get through the rest of the day.

Her shift started with handover from the overnight staff, who'd let her know which patients were particularly sick or particularly difficult. With a long list of people to see, she'd then embark on her morning rounds. There were wounds that needed cleaning and re-bandaging, medication that needed to be handed out, crusty sweaty skin that needed to be washed down with warm cloths, and bedpans and dirty sheets that needed changing. She did it all with a smile – the same smile she'd conjured while looking at herself in the bathroom mirror that morning. The afternoon rounds were just as busy, leaving Bridget barely any time for a break. Or as the Irish girls would say, 'I've barely had time to scratch me arse!' But in many ways, Bridget's patients kept her going. They were all sick or injured and often confined to their hospital beds. Some of them would spend the rest of their short lives in St Ann's, and never so much as step out of their beds for that matter. Focusing on them and their problems meant Bridget forgot about her own.

After work, Bridget spent her nights in the common room at the nurses' home. She'd sit in front of the television, staring at the screen, barely muttering a word to the girls around her. They would laugh and chat and gossip among themselves. But it was all just inaudible noise to Bridget. She'd just stare at the screen in front of her, telling herself the same thing, over and over again – *it's not true.*

'Bridget!' one of the girls would yell from the doorway. 'Phone!'

For two weeks, that happened every night at 8 p.m.

'It's your man, Amir,' they'd say.

'Oh ... tell him I'm not here,' Bridget would reply as her heart pounded and breath shortened.

Every night he'd ring, and every night she'd refuse to talk to him. But he didn't give up – Bridget knew the same thing would happen again the following evening.

Weeks turned into months, and nothing in her daily routine changed. She felt sick in the mornings, pushed through her hectic rounds in the hospital, and went home and quietly sat in the common room, before one of the girls would come in and yell out that Amir was on the phone. She barely left St Ann's in that time. She felt safe within the confines of the hospital precinct, so she never ventured outside of the big grey walls. The city streets she once thrived on exploring were now just a view out of her dorm room window. Her room had become a cell and she a prisoner. But at least as a prisoner she was safe from Amir.

It was Tuesday night, just before 8 p.m. It had been a few days since Amir had last called the nurses' home. Bridget was sitting on the sofa watching *Coronation Street* on the little black-and-white television with some of the other nurses. Colette, who'd barely spoken to Bridget in months, marched into the common room, her nose turned up.

'Bridget,' she said. 'Can I have a wee chat?'

Colette was standing with one hand on her hip, the other leaning on the back of the sofa.

'He's on the phone,' she said. 'He's desperate. The poor thing. Can't you just have a chat to him?'

'I ... ah ... well ... ahh,' Bridget muttered, her mouth dry, her palms sweaty.

'Bridget,' Colette continued. 'It's hard for *me*! You know, because of Jamal. Amir's always asking him about ye. He just wants to see ye. That's all.'

Bridget's cheeks burned. *He doesn't just want to see me. He wants to own me.*

'I can't see him,' she said. 'I'm sorry. It's too hard.'

'Jesus Christ,' Colette said, shaking her head.

Brenda was sitting at the table in the corner, steam rising from a fresh cup of tea in front of her. She'd been listening in to Bridget and Colette's conversation.

'Are you alright, Bridget?' she asked.

'I'm ... yes ... I'm fine, thanks.'

'No, you're not,' Brenda said. 'You're shaking.'

Bridget noticed that her hands and jaw were, in fact, trembling.

'Do you want me to talk to him?' Brenda asked.

Bridget noticed Colette's dark brown eyes narrowed and staring straight at her, as though outraged Bridget would even consider accepting Brenda's help.

'I'll tell him where to go, if you want me to,' Brenda continued.

Bridget nodded, accepting the offer of intervention. Brenda stood up from the table and stormed out of the room like a woman on a mission. Colette forced a dramatic sigh, turned her back on Bridget, and then left the room as well.

Bridget tried to calm herself. But she couldn't, not while Amir was on the line on the communal telephone. *He'll never stop,* she thought. *He'll never let me be.* The last time she'd spoken to Amir was hard enough. And that was ages ago. She feared if he merely *heard* her voice again, it would give him reason, or motivation, to keep calling for yet another few months.

About five minutes passed before Brenda returned to the common room. She sat back down at the table and was about to take a sip of her now cold tea. Bridget turned to her, waiting for her to say something, anything.

'You won't be hearing from him again,' Brenda said casually, before sipping her tea and scrunching her face at the taste of it.

'What'd he say?' Bridget asked.

'Never mind, love. We all see the way you act when he calls. Don't worry about bloody Colette. You don't deserve that shite. And you deserve better than him. Trust me, he's not going to bother you again. And if he does, you let me know.' Brenda winked at Bridget before taking off to make another cup of tea.

She never did find out what Brenda said to Amir that night.

But a day passed without him calling the nurses' home. Then a week. Then a month. Whatever Brenda said, it seemed to have scared him off. Bridget appeared to finally be free from the hold Amir had on her. But she didn't feel free. Her life had become so monotonous, it was hard to tell when one day ended and the next started. Wake up, throw up, work, sleep, repeat. Wake up, throw up, work, sleep, repeat. Wake up, throw up, work, sleep, repeat. Four months had passed since the sickness first came on and there was no relief in sight.

The next phone call she received at the home was from her mother. Bridget's parents had recently moved to Bradford in the north of England, where they were living in a townhouse. Bridget figured it was their quest for a change of scenery after spending their entire lives in the same house in Belmullet.

'How are ye keeping?' Bridget's mammy asked over the phone.

'Grand,' Bridget lied. 'How's yourselves?'

'Oh, grand. Your father misses the sea, of course. But the house is better for it without the stench of fish guts stinkin' it out all the time. Lord above, I won't miss that. There's a few drunkards at the end of the street here, though. Always plastered on a Friday night, God help us. No doubt drinking their dole away. And then causing a ruckus in the street and slashing out the front of houses. No respect. Ah, but thank God there are some good Catholics next door to us. They had us over for tea the other day, God bless 'em. Lovely couple from Dublin who moved here a few years back. No kids. No, the Lord never brought them any. Your father's in good form. He's workin' with your brother in town on a building site. He's out in the jakes at the moment, otherwise I'd put him on. There's always work going here. I s'pose that's why there's so many of us that come over. Not since the war has there been so many Irish in England. Still, it's not the same as Belmullet. Not the same! To be honest, I imagine we'll move back there sooner or later. Your sister wrote us not long ago by the way. She's well. Says it's stinkin' hot in Australia. But she's thankful she's found her calling in the nunnery. With God's help, she'll come back and visit some day soon. Anyway, I'm going on, am'nt I? So are ye all ready then?'

Bridget had long since tuned out. Her mammy was prone to talking non-stop, jumping from topic to topic, for minutes on end without a return word being uttered. Bridget was used to it. But she'd stopped paying attention on this occasion because that familiar sickly churning feeling had returned to her gut.

'I'm sorry, Mammy, what d'ya mean *ready*?' Bridget said.

'You gotta be coddin' me. You don't remember? Your twenty-first birthday. The party! There's only two weeks to go.'

'Oh ...' Bridget said, trying to mask her surprise. 'Of course!'

'Ah, it will be good craic. The boys will be here. And your father, God bless him, can't wipe the smile off his face when he talks about it.'

'Ah ... yes,' Bridget said. 'I ... can't wait to get up there and see all of ya.'

There was a brief silence.

'Are you alright?' her mammy asked. 'You sound under the weather.'

'Oh, no,' Bridget said. 'No, I'm fine, Mammy. Just had a long day.'

'Alright then,' her mammy said, not sounding convinced. 'I wouldn't want ye coming down with something before you get here. Everyone will be lookin' forward to seein' ye. It would be an awful shame if ye weren't looking your best.'

'Don't ye be worrying, Mammy. I'll be in fine form. Just need a good night's sleep. That's all.'

'Grand. Oh, would you look at the time? The neighbours are comin' for tea. I must let ye go. Stay well, dear. I'll be seein' you soon. God bless.'

'God bless,' Bridget said as she hung up the phone, before resting her head against the wall. *The party!* Her twenty-first birthday – she'd completely forgotten about it. It was 7 p.m., but the sickness had well and truly come on. It didn't usually hit this late in the day. She suspected the thought of going back to see her parents was the cause of it.

Two weeks passed after the phone call, with the days going by just as they had in the previous months. Monotonous, slow, with sickness on one side, sleep on the other. Every day was a carbon copy of the one that preceded it. She could feel her birthday party approaching, like ominous storm clouds on the horizon, and she was out in the open, right in its path, with no shelter to hide within. She certainly couldn't hide at St Ann's any more within the safety of its big grey walls. On her final night in London, before returning to see her parents, she couldn't fall asleep. She lay in her bed with the sheets pulled up to her neck, her eyes wide open and staring at the brown stains on the ceiling. *What if Amir sees me out there? What if I get sicker? What will Mammy and Daddy say? What if I never feel better? That's it ... I'll* NEVER *feel better.* She lay awake for hours, tossing and turning from side to side, trying in vain to stop those shambolic thoughts. Eventually, the sun's golden rays started creeping into the gaps between the window and curtain; the sound of trucks on their morning deliveries came from beyond it. The day had come when Bridget would have to face her parents. And as she lay there, wide awake after a sleepless night, with the dawn breaking outside, there was only one remaining thought in her head – *it's not true.*

CHAPTER FOUR

WHAT WILL THE NEIGHBOURS SAY?

Bridget arrived in Bradford with her illness persisting. Like a relentless stray dog seeking companionship, it followed her wherever she went. Her parents' townhouse was two storeys of dark brown brick plonked in the middle of an entire street of townhouses, all joined together, all exactly the same.

Bridget's mammy opened the door to greet her.

'Hiya, Mammy,' Bridget said, hoping her mother would throw her arms out wide and give her a big hug. But she didn't. She just stood in the doorway with her lips scrunched tight and her arms crossed.

'Come in then,' she finally said, pulling the door wide open to let Bridget through.

Bridget lifted her large case out of the sprinkling rain and followed her mother into the house. Her father was grinning ear to ear when he saw his little girl.

'Hello, love,' he said. He stretched his long arms out wide and wrapped them around Bridget. She squeezed him back, resting her head on his shoulder. It had been so long since she'd seen her father – almost three years earlier when she had left Belmullet as an eighteen-year-old. He had been standing at the end of the road they lived on, next to a neat pile of turf that he had assembled earlier. He took his cap off and held it to his chest as Bridget passed him in the car that was taking her to Dublin, where she would then board a ship to England. His eyes looked bloodshot and glassy, his jaw quivering. Bridget had tried to smile at him before the car turned a corner and went out of sight. But she couldn't. She couldn't escape the sadness in his eyes that day. He'd looked just the same when her older brothers and sister left home before her. He always stood in that exact same spot at the end of the road, in prime position to get a final glimpse of his children before they left the village for good. He was such a strong and fearless man – he would jump into the roaring ocean on a rough day to go fishing without an ounce of hesitation. His hands were coarse and hardened, calloused by a lifetime of heavy lifting and hard labour. He was well over six feet tall and towered over most men but was still more likely to break up a fight instead of starting one. Bridget had always looked up to him, and not just because of his height. And it had broken her heart to see him reduced to tears when she left Belmullet that day. In the years that followed, she yearned to see him again and feel the warmth of his hug. Now that moment had finally come in Bradford. And as she rested her head on his woollen jumper while within his sturdy grip, she didn't feel alone for the first time in months.

The three of them were sitting around the kitchen table drinking tea soon after Bridget's arrival. Her daddy still had a slight grin on his face as he sipped from his cup. Her mammy, on the other hand, just stared at the raindrops trickling down the kitchen window.

'How was the trip up?' her daddy asked.

''Twas fine,' Bridget said.

'Are ye excited for the big night?' he asked.

'I am, surely. Will be good craic. Good to see everyone.'

'Ah, it will be grand,' he said. 'Shame we can't all be in Belmullet, but 'twill still feel like home, havin' everyone together. The boys will be happy to see ya.'

The thought of seeing her brothers made Bridget's stomach churn. *What if they find out what's wrong with me?*

'How are ye enjoying it here?' she asked, looking from her father to her mother, who was still staring out the window.

'Ah, it's okay,' her daddy said as he pulled out his pipe and began stuffing tobacco into it. ''Tis a nice little change. There's plenty of work around here for any man that wants it. But I can't imagine we'll be livin' here too long. Belmullet will always be home, ye know.'

'Speakin' of work,' her mammy said, still looking away, 'there's plenty of it to be done in this house. You might be turning twenty-one, but you'll still hafta help your mother and father around the house. I've got some chores for ye, after your bag's put away.'

'Ah, there's no rush,' her daddy said as he lit up his pipe and took a solid puff. 'Me little girl's home for the first time in years. The cleanin' can wait.'

Bridget's mammy's face tightened as she looked across the table at her husband.

'The house isn't going to clean itself. I can't be workin' on me hands and knees all day at my age. Lord above, any daughter should be thankful they're in a house to clean at all and not out on the street with the tinkers in the rain.'

'Of course, Mammy,' Bridget said. 'I'll get to work. Tis no bother.'

She was on her hands and knees scrubbing the grime off the bathroom floor within the hour. And she was cleaning every day in the week that followed. Her mother had her dusting every surface in the house, from the windowsills, to the family photos that filled the mantle, to all the teacups hanging in the kitchen. When she wasn't dusting, she was mopping, scrubbing, sweeping ... then dusting again. There was always something to be done – according to her mother, at least. Bridget barely left the townhouse in that first week. When she wasn't cleaning, she spent her time in her room at the top of the stairs. At least in there she could hide from her mother and father when she felt the sickness coming on. She'd always have a paper bag hidden away in her case for whenever the nausea hit without warning and she couldn't get to the bathroom in time to throw up. In the mornings, she would get up before dawn and sneak downstairs to the toilet to be sick before her parents woke. She'd then hide in her room until she felt well enough to join them for tea in the kitchen.

It's not true. It's not true. It's not true. Bridget kept telling herself that in Bradford. She didn't have to force herself to think it any more. It just came on its own. It crept up whenever she sat idle or when she tossed and turned each night before finally finding the elusive sleep she was so desperately looking for. Bridget's mammy barely said a word to her during that first week. And when she did, it was usually a snide remark or nasty comment. 'Ye missed the dust on top of the mantle ... Start the fire would ye, this place is freezin'... Look at the state of ye, fix your hair and put some proper clothes on before you set foot outa this house ... You're coddin' me if you think that lavatory's clean. Go back and give it another wipe ... Fix some tea for your mother and father will ye ... Go on, hurry up, get a move on, quicker, not clean enough, get the sour look off ye face ...' She never said the things Bridget wanted to hear, like 'good morning', or 'goodnight', or 'thank you so much for all the work you're doing around the house', or 'it's so good to have you here, Bridget. We love you so much.'

A day before her twenty-first birthday party, Bridget's daddy came into her room to chat to her about her mother's behaviour.

'Don't ye be worrying about her,' he said. 'She's just going through the change of life.'

Bridget had learnt in her nursing training that *change of life* meant menopause – the inevitable emotional rollercoaster that awaits all women as they mature.

'Your mother loves ye,' he continued. 'As do I. But God help us, I wouldn't be messing with her when she's in this state. She'd knock the gob right off me if ever I talked back. She's a fierce woman, your mother.'

'It's fine, Daddy,' Bridget said.

'Ah, I pray that relief will come to her soon. With all the hormones flyin' about and everything. And with God's help, it will. But for now, we just need to behave ourselves around her, God bless her.'

He grinned and gave Bridget a wink. She felt an urge to wrap her arms around her father and cry onto his shoulder. He'd make her feel better, surely. He could fix everything. *No, I have to be strong,* she thought as she forced a smile (much like she did when looking in the mirror every morning before starting work on the wards of St Ann's General Hospital).

As she lay in bed that night, she kept going over what her father had said. She wondered if her mother's *change of life* really was the reason she'd been so nasty. And then a question entered

Bridget's mind that made for yet another sleepless night – *does she already know what's wrong with me?*

Bridget had always regarded her birthday as a time of joy and excitement. But this one felt different. Yes, she felt older. But not because it was her birthday. She'd felt older every day during the previous months as she carried this sickness, like she was ageing at an unnaturally quick rate. The only present she wanted for her twenty-first birthday was to feel better ... and for all of this to go away.

On the night of her birthday, 18 March, the family went to a nearby church hall around the corner from the house. The party was in a small room connected to the side of the church. It was freezing cold inside and smelled stale, like old shoes. Bridget's parents and three of her brothers and their wives were there for the celebration. Her mammy had also invited their neighbours, the lovely Catholics from Dublin, to come along. Bridget felt surprisingly comfortable in her loose, long blue dress. It hung down to her ankles, covering every part of her from the neck below. She hadn't felt nauseas since the morning, which meant she'd probably be able to stomach the corned beef, thick bacon, mashed potatoes, boiled cabbage, and broccoli that lined the large table in the middle of the room. With the sounds of laughter and chatter bouncing off the walls and the delicious smells of cooked meat and veggies hanging in the air, she felt a sense of normality that she hadn't experienced in some time. They ate until their bellies were full and sticking out, Bridget's probably more so than everyone else. Her daddy then pulled his chair out from the head of the table, screeching it across the wooden floorboards, getting everyone's attention. He cleared his throat and closed his deep-ocean-blue eyes, then opened his mouth and sang. Everyone sat in silence, staring at him, appearing mesmerised by his angelic voice. Bridget felt the hairs on her arms standing up and tears forming in the corner of her eyes. She looked over at her mother, who also had a glisten in her eyes. Music had always been a staple of their family gatherings. And after her father sang a couple of songs, the music didn't stop as the night went on. The hall was bursting with the vibrations of toe-tapping beats, the hair-raising tones of the fiddle and flute, and the poetic lyrics of Irish folklore. There was laughter and dancing. And boy, did they dance. Bridget felt so free, so untroubled, as she twirled and tapped on the creaky wooden floorboards of the little church hall to the songs of her homeland. She felt as though she was back home in Belmullet before she ever left for London, back when she was pure and naïve, but safe from the outside world. The night was like a dream. But it wasn't like some of the frightening dreams she'd been having lately. This night, she was with her family celebrating adulthood. And for the first time in months, she wasn't worried about hiding the sickly feeling from everyone around her. She wasn't trapped, terrified, and alone. All was well, just like it used to be.

After the party, Bridget had one more week in Bradford with her parents before she'd have to return to London. Then it would be back to the daily grind of sleep, sickness, and work. Much like her first week in Bradford, she spent most of the second week in her room (when she wasn't cleaning, that was). The sickness continued to come in the pre-dawn darkness before easing in time for morning tea with her mother and father. Her mother's *change of life* didn't seem to improve during the week after the party. Her mammy was just as nasty to Bridget, even though she was now twenty-one – a proper adult.

The day before Bridget was due to leave Bradford, she walked into the kitchen mid-morning, looking just as dishevelled as she was feeling: pale as a ghost, her hair frizzy and all over the place, her eyes drooping and bloodshot. Her mammy was sitting at the kitchen table drinking tea.

'What's the matter with ye?' she howled in Bridget's direction, as though she'd been waiting for days to say it. 'If there's something wrong, go to the doctor!'

'I'm okay, Mammy.'

Her mother said nothing. Her eyes narrowed as she looked Bridget up and down, studying every part of her.

'Your hair!' she said. 'It looks terrible. Come here, I'm going to wash it.'

Her mammy began clearing teacups and dishes from the sink and dumping them on the bench. She turned the tap on and pulled a chair over. Bridget sat down and lowered her head into the sink. Her frizzy, curled strawberry blonde locks sprung out and filled the basin. Her mammy grabbed hold of the back of her head and pushed it under the water. It was icy-cold on Bridget's scalp, trickling down the side of her face, making her shiver. Her mammy roughly pulled her head out of the icy-cold water again. She then poured warm water over Bridget's head before running her fingers through the frizzy hair, ripping through knots without warning. Bridget was clenching her teeth together, her eyes scrunched shut, desperately trying not to gasp, not to react in any way. Her mammy squeezed shampoo into her hair and roughly rubbed it in, forming a thick layer of suds. Bridget was being pushed and pulled from side to side, backwards and forwards, her head scraping the side of the basin as her mammy manoeuvred it.

'Jesus, Mary, and Joseph!' her mammy said. 'Look at all these knots!'

Bridget winced as her mother pulled at the biggest knot yet, and probably a dozen or so hairs with it.

'You haven't been yourself. Sittin' around the house all day, asleep in the bed. God help us, you're young! You should be out and about.'

She tried to answer but was forced to clamp her mouth shut instead as her mammy pulled out another knot.

'What in Lord's name is wrong with ye then?'

Bridget braced herself at what she was about to say as the warm sudsy water splashed around her.

'I missed my period,' she said.

Silence. Her mammy stopped washing her hair; in fact, she stopped moving altogether. They both seemed to freeze – Bridget with her head stuck to the sink, her mammy standing behind her, over her. Bridget still couldn't bear to open her eyes even though she'd only be looking at the bottom of the basin. They were both so still, so quiet, it was as though they weren't even there in that moment.

'Argh!' her mother grunted, breaking the awful silence. 'Look at the cut of ye. The gorgeous head of hair you've got and this is the way you look after it. Other girls would kill for hair like yours. You need to show a bit of pride in yeerself.'

Bridget waited for her mother to say something about her missed period. But she didn't. She simply continued to wash her hair – poking, prodding, pulling, scraping. It got rougher as she went on, until finally she stepped away from the sink and said, 'There ye go. Now you hafta be lookin' after it yourself in London. Have a bitta pride.'

Bridget's mammy left her alone in the kitchen. She wanted to cry. She'd wanted to cry the entire time. Her head felt red raw as though her mammy had tried to rip the hair from her scalp, and her neck was tender from all the pushing and pulling. She lifted herself from the sink and returned to the safety of her room at the top of the stairs. Her hair was now cleaner than it had been in months, but pain festered at its roots. She was hurting, not just from the throbbing of her scalp but also because of what she'd said to her mother – and the silence she'd got in return.

On her final night in Bradford, there was a knock at Bridget's door. It was her daddy. He closed the door behind him and sat on the end of her bed. He exhaled heavily and rested his dinner-plate-sized hands on his knees.

'Is everything alright?' he asked softly, in his deep gravelly voice.

Bridget felt her heart rate picking up, and her eyes began darting around the room.

'Of course, Daddy,' she said, nowhere near as calmly as she'd intended to sound.

Her daddy tapped his large hand on the bed beside him, gesturing for Bridget to scoot up and sit next him, just like she used to as a child when she needed consoling.

'Are ye sure now?' he asked.

Bridget couldn't bring herself to look at her father. That would set her off.

'I'm ... alright, Daddy. I'm just feeling a bit off. I must have picked up something from the hospital.'

There was a glisten of drops on his lashes. His big ocean-blue eyes were surrounded by redness – the same state they'd been in when Bridget left Belmullet three years earlier. His back was hunched over, his head bowed towards the floor. He looked small, or rather normal-sized, with this sort of posture. Either way, he didn't look like the gentle giant that he usually appeared to be.

'I love ye very much,' he said. 'If there is something wrong ... I mean, for goodness sake, ... you're me daughter ... God help us ... you might be twenty-one, but yeer still me little girl.'

He looked up from the floor towards Bridget. She desperately wanted to tell him about her missed period, about her sickness, about Amir and the way he treated her. But she feared he might react the same way her mother did. Or worse, it might break his heart.

'I'm fine, Daddy,' she finally said. 'I love you.'

He forced a smile back at her but had the same despairing look in his eyes. She always loved the sight of his smile. But not like this. She never wanted him to look at her like this again.

The next morning, Bridget woke before the sun rose. She joined her daddy and her older brother in the kitchen, where they were in the midst of their pre-dawn ritual of tea and toast before work. They would be taking her to the train station and then heading to a construction site on the other side of town. Her mother was still in bed, so she wouldn't have a chance to say a proper goodbye.

Bridget sat in the back of her brother's car, her dad in the front seat, on the way to the train station. As the golden glow of the sun's rays began creeping over the horizon, she could feel the dreaded sensation of queasiness stirring within her. It was at the top of her stomach, rising up, and then it was at the back of her throat. It was a great big ball of pressure and there was no stopping it. She clasped her hands to her mouth, breathing through her nose, trying to stay calm. The acidy taste hit her tongue and she knew there would be no stopping it. She hunched over, quickly unzipping her case and scrounging around her clothes until she finally found her laundry bag. Her mouth was now full of vomit, and it was about to explode everywhere. She quickly threw up into the laundry bag, supressing her urge to gasp loudly. She'd become quite good at throwing up quietly during the previous months. She slowly lifted her head to see if her daddy and brother had noticed what was happening in the back seat. Her brother had his hands on the wheel and eyes on the road. Her father was humming and staring out the window. Both were apparently oblivious to her early morning misery.

Another burst of sick rose up and came out her mouth. Then another. Then another. It was still quite dark in the back seat, apart from the occasional yellow glimmer of the street lights flickering through the window. But it was not enough light to expose what was happening to her. She was relieved in one sense – that her daddy and brother couldn't see her being sick. But their obliviousness to the situation unfolding behind them also made her feel alone. They were so close, just a few feet away in the front of the car. But they couldn't reach out and hold her and tell her everything would be okay. Her mother, too, couldn't be there for her, to pat her shoulder and hold her hair back as she threw up. Bridget was all alone in the darkness of the back seat, with the lining of her stomach now lining the inside of her laundry bag.

By the time they arrived at the train station fifteen minutes later, her eyes were watering profusely, her tongue burned with acidity, she was light-headed, and she still felt that lump at the back of her throat. She got out of the car and stepped into the cold morning air. Her brother got out and gave her a goodbye hug. Her daddy did the same. Her head rested on the warm wool of his jumper as he wrapped his long arms around her. They held each other tightly, and for a moment, everything in the world seemed all right once more. She didn't want to let go. Then that urge to cry came back, as though it had never left. He kissed her forehead and let her go.

'Love ya,' he said, towering over her.

'Love you too, Daddy.'

'God bless.' He opened the car door and got inside.

They were gone and Bridget was alone again, standing on the platform of a near-empty train station in the early morning dimness. The lump in her throat had disappeared, as had her urge to spew. She lugged her case along the platform, finding shelter from the chilling wind behind a large brick column. And there, under the hefty clock, she waited for her train, her mind all over the place.

You should have told them ... No, you can never tell them ... They need to know ... It will break their hearts if they know ... You can't do this alone ... You'll be alone forever if they know what you've done ... You should have told them ... No, you shouldn't have ... Yes, you should have ... No, you shouldn't have ... Yes, you should have ... No, you shouldn't ... Help ... Lord, help me.

With each tick of the clock that hung over the platform, her mind went back and forth. The train eventually emerged from a bend and screeched to a halt on the tracks in front of her. She was leaving Bradford as a twenty-one-year-old, an adult. But she was still too scared to tell her parents the truth. *But it's not true,* she quickly told herself. The train headed south, winding its way through the English countryside for three hours on its way to London. She stared out the window as the blur of green fields and grey towns zipped past. Her mind was still racing, far quicker than the train along the tracks. While she was still alone and in denial, her trip to Bradford had at least taught her one thing: her parents would not hold the answers to her problems.

She arrived back in London more broken than when she left. But her life in the big city was just the same as it had been before. She was once again comfortable (or as close to comfortable as she could be) living within the safety of St Ann's big grey walls. Each day came in the same fashion, with Bridget hurling up in the hospital toilets. And each day ended with Bridget in her bed, trying to escape the thoughts that had followed her around since morning. Sleep was her only saviour. She felt as though she was merely getting by, not *living* as she once had. She didn't look forward to nights out with friends, or her next trip home to see her family, or knock-off time after a long shift in the hospital. In fact, she didn't look forward to anything. It was a poor excuse of an existence, but at least, she figured, she was finding a way to exist.

It was a Friday night, a couple of weeks after Bridget had got back from Bradford. She was sitting in the common room at the nurses' home with a cup of hot tea on the table in front of her, the murmurs of gossiping girls and a blaring television filling the room.

'Phone for ye, Bridget!' a voice yelled from the corridor. Her chest tightened. *Amir! Not again.* She instantly felt stuck to the chair – unable to get up, even if she wanted to. It had been months since Amir had called. But the very thought of him still struck the same familiar fear into her.

Bridget picked up the phone and slowly put it to her ear. 'Hello?' she said.

'Bridget, dear.' The voice of a woman came through. 'How are ya? What's the craic?'

She recognised the voice straight away. It was her Aunty Ellen, her mammy's younger sister, who also lived in London. Bridget had only caught up with Ellen a few times during her three years in London. And she hadn't spoken to her at all in the past year, so the sound of her voice over the phone caught Bridget a bit by surprise.

'I'm grand, Aunty Ellen. How are you?'

'Ah, very well dear,' Aunty Ellen said. 'I've been speaking with your mother. 'Twould be lovely to see you, Bridget.'

'Oh, of course, Aunty Ellen. That'd be nice.'

'There's a café near King's Cross,' Ellen said. 'Not far from me place. Tis a nice little walk. I think you'd like it. How about you meet me there tomorrow morning?'

'Ah sure,' Bridget said. 'I have the day off, so tis no bother.'

'God bless you, Bridget. Meet me at nine. Don't be late. The name of the café is Hummingbird. You can't miss it. God bless ye.'

The next morning, Ellen was already sitting at the table when Bridget arrived at the café. Her dark blue eyes were glued to Bridget as she approached. Ellen's dyed chestnut hair was freshly permed. She was wearing a long flowery dress, stockings, a grey cloche hat, and a black coat – an outfit worthy of her Sunday finest. She got to her feet and eyed Bridget up and down. It was a strange look – the sort a doctor might give to a patient when examining them.

'Oh Lord,' Ellen said. 'It's been too long, my dear.'

She sat back down and gestured with her hand for Bridget to do the same. Ellen was smiling rather forcefully, revealing missing teeth behind the corners of her lips. They sat in silence for a moment, Ellen still staring – that same piercing gaze, apparently blink-less and focused entirely on Bridget as though there was nothing else in the room.

'And how's the nursing life treating ya?' she asked.

'Ah, I can't complain,' Bridget said. 'Learning lots. The girls I work with are great craic.'

'That's lovely,' Ellen said. 'And seeing all that sickness in the hospital must make you thank the Lord for your own health.'

'Oh, of course,' Bridget said, her cheeks starting to burn.

'And how *is* your health, Bridget? Are you well?' Ellen's eyes darted down towards Bridget's stomach and then back up to her face.

'Ah, I'm grand,' Bridget said as calmly as she could, despite the growing fire in her cheeks.

There was a moment of awkward silence, which was finally filled by a waitress bringing over two cups and a large pot of tea. Ellen poured her tea and took a sip, then spoke as though she simply couldn't keep her words in any longer.

'There's one ting I hafta say, dear,' she confessed. 'Your mother and father are worried about ye. *Terribly* worried. They came to see me actually.'

'They came here? To London?' Bridget said, shocked and a little hurt they hadn't come to see their youngest daughter.

'Oh aye, Bridget. They're terribly worried, yeer parents. Yeer mother said ye were not yourself when ye went to see them in Bradford. And I must say, dear ... I don't mean to gawk, but ye don't *look* too well.'

Bridget couldn't find any words to respond. The burning sensation in her cheeks went from mild to blistering.

'Perhaps, dear,' Ellen continued, before taking a sip of her tea. 'Perhaps ... ye might be pregnant.'

Bridget froze. The fire had now spread beyond her cheeks to the rest of her face. Her throat felt as dry and coarse as sandpaper, rendering her incapable of responding.

'But don't ye be worrying, Bridget. We have a *plan*, dear. Nobody needs to know.'

Bridget looked down at the tea in front of her. She couldn't bring herself to face Ellen as she spoke.

'This can stay between us,' Ellen continued. 'Bridget, *I* will take the baby. No one will know. It will be mine for all they know.'

Bridget stirred her tea with the spoon, not taking her eyes off the milky spirals that filled the cup. She could still feel Ellen's gaze upon her. *It's not true* – that was the thought that came into Bridget's head, instinctively, just as it had done so many times during the previous months. But it suddenly didn't seem to hold the same weight it did before. It was now just a thought, with no substance to it, no possibility of truth attached to it. Bridget realised, or rather accepted, at this moment that those three little words she'd been telling herself – *it's not true* – were a lie.

'Jaysus,' Ellen continued. 'Sure, there are priests that can hear your confession and give ye penance. But Lord help us, Bridget, you gotta think about your mother and father. How's all this going to reflect on them?'

Bridget could feel her bottom lip quivering, so she bit down on it. She didn't want to hear any more. She was on the verge of pulling out her chair and running from the café.

'What do ye say, Bridget? Tis the only way. Let *me* take the baby. For the family. C'mon now, ye need to ask yeerself, if this gets out ... Lord help us if it does ... but if it does get out ... what will the neighbours say?'

Silence. Bridget swirled her tea some more and then looked up at Ellen. 'I'm fine, Aunty Ellen. Just been unwell is all.'

Ellen's face dropped, the muscles in it drooping like a fast-melting ice cream. 'Oh, I see,' she said. She cast another look down at Bridget's stomach in a way that seemed to say *You can't lie to me.* 'You're sure?' she said, so slowly and drawn out it almost sounded like her voice had been slowed down on a record player.

Bridget nodded, even managing a smile. 'Thanks for your

concern, Aunty Ellen. God bless ye for thinking about me. But I'm grand.'

Ellen pushed her cup into the middle of the table and cast away her piercing gaze for the first time since Bridget had walked in. And with that, their morning tea was over. She left Bridget alone in the café with the realisation she'd been fighting for six months: *I am pregnant.*

Bridget was still trembling as she sat on the tube on her way back to St Ann's. *I am pregnant. I AM pregnant. I AM PREGNANT. I. AM. PREGNANT.* Through months of sickness and sorrow, she had not been able to summon that thought. Surely it existed somewhere in her mind. But it was so deeply buried, so meticulously concealed with denial, that she was able to simply get through the mundanity of each day without thinking it. Of course, she'd known it to be true that entire time. She must have. Especially given the words had been spoken aloud to her by a doctor, months earlier – 'Miss Reilly, you're pregnant.' But for some reason, her mind couldn't process this information as fact until it was delivered by her Aunty Ellen in that café in King's Cross. As the tube wound its way through the underground darkness, another realisation hit Bridget – her parents knew. And not only that, but they'd conjured a plan that would see her baby taken from her and raised in another home.

She had seen it all before. Back home in Ireland, a family in a town not far from Belmullet had once been faced with the same predicament. Sarah Fagan was a young girl who lived in a tiny house with her older sister and their parents. But Sarah's mother and father were much older than most parents. They would have been in their mid-forties by the time Sarah was born. Bridget never thought much of it. But there were always whispers around town that Sarah was not who they said she was. Sure, she was a

Fagan. But not to her parents. They were, in fact, her grandparents. Sarah's real mother was Val Fagan, who she'd believed to be her older sister for her entire life. Val had given birth to Sarah out of wedlock as a teenager. So, Sarah's grandparents had raised her as their own, telling everyone in town the Lord had gifted them a miracle child in what should have been their retiring years.

One day, as a sixteen-year-old, someone in town told Sarah who her real mother was – her supposed older sister, Val. At first, Sarah didn't believe it. But then she started noticing the little looks people gave her around town. The muffled whispers surrounding her seemed to become louder and louder and followed her wherever she went. She eventually realised that shame had been brought upon the Fagan name because of her arrival into the world. And that burden bore down upon her. It was a crushing weight of lies and judgement that could never be lifted.

Now Bridget was being asked to hide her child and live a lie, just like the Fagans. *There is no way I will let that happen,* she thought as she arrived back at St Ann's after her encounter with Ellen. *I'm having a baby and I'm going to keep it.*

PRESENT

CHAPTER 5

NANNY

'I don't want to be putting any of that in the story,' Mum says to me over the phone.

'What?' I say. 'It has to be. We can't just ignore the way you were treated.'

'Hmm. I'm not sure, Dan. I don't want to mention Ellen or the plan they had or anything like that. I think it's better if we leave it out of the book.'

'But, Mum,' I say. 'Please, just listen to me for a moment. If we just ignore the way they treated you ... *they* win. They've silenced you, just like they wanted.'

'Oh yes ...' she says. 'But I don't want to upset anyone.'

'Upset anyone? What about the way they treated you? You shouldn't be worried about upsetting anyone.'

'What about my poor mother, Dan? She's just an old woman now. I don't want the story to reflect badly on her.'

I stop walking and peer out at the moonlight on the sprawling Swan River that runs through the heart of Perth. The white glow is rippling across the surface like a flag in the wind. The path I'm on is empty and almost pitch-black apart from the light of my phone. I've been speaking to Mum through my headphones for the past hour. She'd just finished telling me all about the way her mother treated her when she went home for the first time after falling pregnant. The rejection, the scheming, the secrecy, all important parts of telling her story properly – in my opinion, anyway. But throughout the entire process of writing her story, Mum has been more concerned about divulging information that could be deemed as disrespectful to her mother.

'Maybe we should just leave it there for tonight, Mum,' I say.

'Yes. I think so.'

'Are you okay?' I ask. I always feel the need to ask this during our phone calls. My biggest fear is that she'll hang up and burst into tears, then spiral into a depression that's been sitting dormant for decades.

'I'm fine, dear,' she says. 'Okay, talk to you soon. Love you, bye. Bye. Bye. Bye.' (She always says 'bye' more than necessary at the end of a conversation. I think it might be an Irish thing.)

We both hang up. Beeping fills my headphones and then there's silence, apart from the gentle sound of water splashing along the bank of the river. We've been having these phone calls for months, every Sunday night, and sometimes during the week as well. Some of our chats have been groundbreaking. Mum has been able to recite events from her past as though they have just happened. Like the car ride to the train station when she was leaving Bradford. She remembered every little detail about that, as though the sickly feeling was stirring within her as she was reciting it. Who would have thought a nauseous car ride could remain so vividly in someone's memory for more than forty years?

But then there have been major events that Mum has entirely forgotten, like the moment she found out she was pregnant. She simply can't remember that exact moment. Whether the memory has just decayed to nothingness over time, or whether it's something that she's buried because it's just too painful to recall, she hasn't been able to explain it. So I've had to try to fill in the gaps where Mum's recollection has failed to fire. But forgotten memories aside, the thing that has really challenged me during our phone calls has been the details Mum *can* remember but wants to leave out of her story – most notably, the details about her mother and the plan they conjured to take Mum's baby and raise it in secrecy. Mum seems afraid to speak the truth. It's as though the shame still has a hold on her, even after more than forty years.

I start running along the path. It's so dark, it's hard to see what's on the ground in front of me. As I gather speed, I try to dodge the bursting bits of pavement that have been pushed up by tree roots. I'm now almost sprinting, bouncing off my toes, which still have blisters from my last run. My breathing intensifies as I make a sharp left and then turn onto a dimly lit and carless road that lines the river. My heartbeat increases, my breath shortens. *Argh.* My muscles ache, my chest tightens. *Just push to that tree*, I tell myself. *Just fifty more metres. Just push.* I stride out. Long heavy steps that become heavier every time my foot hits the ground. *Almost there! Argh. Push! Push!*

I've made it. I reach the tree, or rather the shadow of it, which is cast across the road, its branches shaped like forks of lightning. I pull up and hunch over, gasping heavily as oxygen fills my lungs. This has been my escape: running along Perth's iconic Swan River late at night. In this part of the city, on the east side, it's a beautifully quiet place, and there's barely a runner or dog-walker to be seen at this time of the evening. As I push myself during each run, the sting in my muscles and stabbing of my chest occupies my mind, replacing the image that's been there for months. The image of my mother, pregnant and alone in London. It haunts my dreams and sits at the back of my eyelids when I close my eyes. I can't escape the sorrow of it, the pity of it, but mostly the anger of it. *How could they treat her like that?*

I've now caught my breath, so I pick up the pace to a gentle run. I pass under the spotlight of a street lamp, which has attracted a swarm of erratic moths. My thoughts feel just as erratic. I think about what Mum and I spoke about on the phone a few minutes earlier – her trip to Bradford. The image in my mind of my mother, young and pregnant, suddenly dissolves, giving way to a new image – her mother. My dear old nanny. For most of my life, we've lived on opposite sides of the world. Our relationship has never been more than a quick 'hello' over the phone, or a Christmas or birthday card with a generic message of well wishes. I've only met Nanny once before. It was back when I was eighteen and had just left Australia for the first time. I was on a pilgrimage in Ireland with my brother, Sean, visiting extended family we'd never met and enjoying the sights and warm welcomes of our ancestral homeland. Even a decade later, meeting Nanny is still so fresh in my mind …

Ireland, 2008.

We pull up to Nanny's house in Belmullet after a long cross-country drive. It's the same house that Mum, her brothers, and sister grew up in. It's just as I imagined – a small, white-washed cottage behind a waist-high stone wall and among green hills in the Irish countryside. The air is fresh; the cold stings my face and turns my breath to mist in front of me. I walk over the squelchy, rain-soaked ground towards the front gate, and there she is.

Nanny is at the door. She's standing upright, proud and welcoming, not hunched over like you'd expect from most ninety-year-olds. It looks like she's also done her hair and make-up in preparation for our arrival.

'Jaysus!' she says, smiling, revealing her tea-stained dentures. 'Look at the size of ye. You're all grown up.'

She wraps her arms around Sean and me and ushers us into her house. Within minutes, we are at her kitchen table with searing hot cups of tea and slightly stale biscuits in front of us.

'How'd ye go driving down?' Nanny asks.

'Good,' I say. 'It was a bit of a bumpy drive. But the scenery's nice.'

'I was worried about ye,' she says. 'What with all the ice on the roads and everything. Ye wouldn't be used to that in Australia.'

'It's okay, Nanny,' Sean says. 'We were very careful. Took it nice and slow.'

'Oh, that's grand,' Nanny says. 'But ye don't want to be going too slow or you'll get a lorry up the arse. Talking of roads ... shall we head into town? You boys must be hungry. Are ye hungry?'

'We actually ate on the way down,' I say.

'Ah, you're growing boys,' she says. 'There's always room for more. Drive me into town and I'll cook you both a fry when we get back.'

We don't dare argue with her, especially in her own home.

In town, we take Nanny to the post office, where she picks up her pension money. Then we head to the supermarket and load up on groceries for the days ahead, with enough bacon, eggs, and black pudding for a fried breakfast for every meal if we want. As we're wheeling the shopping out of the supermarket, Nanny approaches me and holds out her hand. I look at it for a moment, unsure what she's doing. Her hands are densely wrinkled, with large brown and white spots covering the backs of them. I take her hand in mine and feel crumpled paper within it. She lets go and clasps my fist shut around the paper. I open it to reveal two fifty-euro notes.

'Oh, Nanny,' I say. 'I can't—'

'Take it!' she says. 'Buy yourself something nice with that. Or sweets ... but not too many otherwise your teeth will fall out, like mine.'

She turns away and jumps into the car before I have a chance to give it back to her. I can't take this. It's her pension money. I plan to slip it into her bag later when she's not looking. As I get into the car, Nanny says, 'And don't ye be trying to give that money back to me again or I'll give ye a kick up the arse. Alright?'

Sean and I stay with Nanny in Belmullet for three nights. During the days, we explore the countryside, walking through the fields and lanes, and along the coast, at times fighting against the stiff ocean breeze and pelting rain. On the second day, Nanny takes us up to the graveyard where Grandad is buried. We stand for a few minutes in front of the grave.

'Oh Jaysus,' Nanny says, sighing. 'He was a great man, your grandad. He would have loved to see ye here.'

Her lips are scrunched tight. She seems to be fighting off tears. 'Jesus, Mary, and Joseph,' she says. 'Ye never know what the Lord has planned for ya. Come on, boys, let's pray for his soul.'

We stand together around his grave, praying (something I only do when I'm forced to) as a gale blows in from the Atlantic. It's strong enough to make me sway off balance. But Nanny stands firmly over her husband's grave. She's an old woman, in her early nineties, but she's still too defiant to be pushed around by a howling wind. I never met Grandad. He died just before I was born. I wonder how many times Nanny has come up here over the years to mourn him. She's spent the entirety of my lifetime grieving the love of her life. It's such a long time to be without the one you love. But still, she stands tall and proud on her ninety-year-old legs at his grave, even in the face of an Atlantic gale.

That night, Sean and I venture into town to experience the atmosphere of an Irish pub – a *proper* Irish pub, unlike some of the so-called Irish pubs in Australia that try to mimic the real thing.

'Behave yourselves tonight, boys,' Nanny says as we leave the house. 'Don't ye be getting plastered.'

'Of course, Nanny,' we both say, smiling.

'I'm not havin' ye on,' she says. 'I don't want to be hearing that you've been up to mischief. Word gets around quick here.' Nanny glares at me for a moment, apparently in no doubt that I'm the trouble-making brother. She grins but I have no doubt she's being serious. 'Have a *lovely* night, boys.'

Sean and I decide to check out a tiny bar called McDonnells. It's on the main street in town but you could walk past it without even knowing it's there. It's nestled in between a funeral home and a chemist. The façade consists of an innocuous black door and little window, with a Guinness sign and 'McDonnells' written above in black writing. I walk inside with Sean, expecting to discover a grand pub that's deceptively larger than the exterior of the building suggests. But no, it's tiny. The bar is about the size of a household kitchen bench, a wall of spirit bottles behind it. Aromas of spilled stout and cigarette smoke rise up from the carpet. The room is dimly lit, the walls cluttered with photos and memorabilia, the floor space filled with tables and chairs, and, of course, local drinkers with pints in hand. Although it's tiny, the pub is warm and has a cosy feel about it. I'm pretty certain this is the best place in town to be for 'good craic'.

Within a few hours, the pub is packed to capacity. There's barely room to move as more and more locals cram in. Sean and I have been drinking all night, but we haven't yet bought a drink. No one will let us buy one when they hear we're from Australia. 'You're Aussies! Ah, that's grand! Lemme get ye a pint!'

Everyone seems to know all about us. Or rather, they know our family. 'Oh, you're Bridget's boys! Lemme get ye a pint ... Oh, you're Maggie Reilly's grandsons! Fine woman, Maggie. Still going strong in her nineties! Lemme get ye a pint.'

In the back of my head (somewhere beyond the alcohol-induced lack of inhibitions), I hear Nanny's voice: 'Don't ye be getting too plastered.' I better take it easy, I think. Even though I'm eighteen now and a proper adult, I'm staying in Nanny's house and I don't want to blatantly disobey her. She did seem pretty serious earlier when she told me not to make a fool of myself. But the pints keep coming in my direction. And who am I to argue with a free drink?

Later in the night, after I down my seventh pint, I stumble through the crowd to the toilet at the back of the pub. My eyes seem to detach from my body as I try to stand in front of the urinal. It seems to be swaying all over the place, like I'm on a ship in rough seas. I realise at this point that I'm absolutely shitfaced – well beyond the point of no-return-to-sobriety. My stomach churns, leading to a deep gulp before an explosion of vomit sprays from my mouth. I lean against the walls, emptying the contents of my stomach into the urinal. I spit out the last bit of vomit and stumble back into the pub, where I'm handed another pint of Guinness. 'Get that into ye!' a bearded stranger says to me. 'Good lad!'

I've already learnt during my travels in Ireland that it's rude to say no when you're offered something. I take a sip of the foamy surface and find a wall to lean on so I don't hit the deck. I need to sober up. Nanny will be pissed off if she finds out I'm blind drunk. She'll probably be ashamed too. Actually, she'll probably bloody kill me.

The night spirals into a blur of pint glasses, Irish folk music, laughter, and the incoherent ramblings of locals. And somewhere in among all of that, I've definitely made a fool of myself – I'll just never be able to remember *how* I did it. At closing time, Sean and I emerge from the pub, arm in arm with our new friends. The laughter and singing of the little bar spills out with us into the empty street, where the cold air doesn't feel nearly as cold as it should thanks to the alcohol in my blood. Sean and I walk up the street, back towards Nanny's place. Just like the urinal earlier, the road in front of me seems to be swaying all over the place.

'You're really pissed,' Sean says, laughing.

'I'm awwlright maaate,' I say. 'I'm not 'ven that drunk.'

Sean laughs. 'Just don't wake Nanny up, okay? She'll kill you.'

'Heeeeeey, do you think Nanny will find out that I drank heeeaps tonight? Do you reckon I made a fooool of myself? Am I in trouble? Shiiiit. She's going to kill me. I've disgraced the family name.'

We make it home thanks to Sean leading the way, which is good because my sense of direction has abandoned me in the darkness. I tip-toe through the house to my bedroom. At least I think I'm tip-toeing (I'm actually bumping into every chair, table, and wall in my erratic path to the bed). I collapse face-first onto the mattress, not even pulling back the sheets to get under them. My head is still spinning violently, but I don't think I'm capable of getting to my feet and going outside to throw up. At least I didn't wake Nanny. She'll hopefully be none the wiser. Then she won't be ashamed. And most importantly, she won't kill me. Sleep comes upon me fairly quickly.

I wake early the next morning with a throbbing headache and a sense of hazy regret. I'm ashamed of how I acted last night. Trouble is, I can't *remember* how I acted last night. I hear the sizzling of a pan on the other side of the wall. I walk into the kitchen to the sound of a boiling kettle and the smell of fried bacon and toasting bread. Sean is at the stovetop, cracking eggs over a pan. Nanny is sitting at the table, still in the warmth of her dressing grown. She gives me a sideways glance as I sit down. I try to act normal, spritely even, despite my throbbing head and churning gut.

'You're up early,' Nanny says to me. 'Did ye have a drink last night?' She takes a sip of her tea. But she's still not looking directly at me.

'I ah ... yeah,' I say gingerly. 'I had a drink.'

'Oh, *a* drink,' she says, her voice rising in pitch. 'You must have woken half the country stumblin' in last night. Louder than a tinker on dole night, you were.'

I look down at the table, guilt growing within me.

'And did ye *behave* yourself at the pub?' Nanny says.

I think back to the countless pints I drank, the moment I was violently sick in the urinal, and then the pints I continued to drink. The rest is a bit of a blur.

'Ahh ... yeah I did, Nanny,' I say in an unconvincing manner.

She takes a sip of her tea and says nothing for a moment. 'Course ye did,' she says. 'You're a good lad. And if ye didn't behave yourself ... well, the neighbours would be tellin' me soon enough. Tis a small town, Belmullet.'

Nanny winks at me and smiles, once again revealing her tea-stained dentures.

The night before Sean and I are due to leave Belmullet, Nanny and I end up having a chat over cups of tea.

'I was meant to come back with Dad,' I say.

Nanny's demeanour darkens. 'He was a good man, your father,' she says, her voice crumbling. 'God rest his soul.'

Tears well in her eyes. I suddenly regret bringing Dad up.

'It's okay,' I say to Nanny. 'He's in a better place now.'

I don't know if I actually believe that. The idea of heaven and hell, life after death – it all seems a bit absurd to me now. But I can't stand to see my poor old grandmother reduced to tears, so I figure it's an appropriate thing to say.

'God rest his soul,' she says again, so softly it's almost a whisper.

Mum and Dad have been separated for well over a decade. But still, Nanny appears distraught at the very mention of her son-in-law – so distraught it's as though he was her own son.

The following morning, we say goodbye to Nanny. Sean and I get a photo with her in the kitchen just before we leave. We crouch down either side of her as she sits at the table, an arm around each of us. Sadly, this will probably be the last photo we'll ever get with her. She's quiet this morning. She's barely said a word since we woke. Poor thing. I feel bad leaving her alone here in the house where she raised six kids with her beloved husband, the love of her life. But now its rooms are empty and quiet. This little home holds so many memories for Nanny. Memories of better times, perhaps some not so great times as well, but memories nonetheless of a time when all of her family was here and under her care.

After hugging Nanny goodbye, Sean and I get in the car and

pull out in front of the house. I look back at the little cottage. Nanny is standing in the doorway, tall and proud, waving enthusiastically. It's an almost Queen-like wave, the way her hand pivots back and forth. There's a huge smile on her face, wide and brimming. But her eyes are glassy and her cheeks are speckled with tears. I wave back and force a smile. But the image of my poor old grandmother, waving with so much vigour and a beaming smile yet with so much sadness in her eyes, stirs despair within me.

Back in the present, a decade later, I'm no longer gasping for air. I walk slowly under Perth's starless sky as I cool down from my run. I'm exhausted. It's been a long day. And the earlier phone call with Mum about her time in Bradford as a young pregnant woman has me feeling emotionally drained. I follow the dimly lit pathway along the river back towards my apartment, where I live with my girlfriend, Jen. I can't stop thinking about Nanny. The image of her in my head, my lasting image of her, is of the old woman I met back when I was eighteen. She was so generous, bringing me and Sean into her home and forcing me to take her pension money. She was so loving, the way she spoke of Grandad at his grave and my father at the kitchen table, and the way she constantly wanted to make sure Sean and I were properly fed and looked after. And she was still a proud woman, concerned about how my drunken antics at the local pub might reflect on the family (thankfully she never did get back to me regarding what she'd found out about my actions that night).

But the image that really sticks with me is the one of Nanny waving goodbye to us from her doorway. Her stoic stance on old legs, her vigorous wave, her endearing smile and longing eyes. It is a wonderful final image to have of a beloved family member. But still, it's so different from that other image of her. The image of the woman who pushed and pulled at Mum's hair in Bradford, ignoring her cries for help about her pregnancy, before conjuring a plan to send her baby away to be raised in secret and fed lies.

As I arrive back at my apartment after my run, I vow to always remember the way Nanny treated Mum in her time of need. I won't hold on to this thought to be bitter or spiteful. I will remember so I never let myself inherit the same pride that consumed my dear old Nanny.

PAST

CHAPTER SIX

THE PLAN

London, 1971.

The moon revealed itself from behind the clouds of the night sky, casting a white glow into Bridget's dorm room. It was midnight and she was wide awake. The hum of cars on nearby roads nagged at her ears like a stubborn mosquito. She rolled back and forth within her starchy sheets, waiting for sleep to come. Her thoughts circled, entwining themselves into an undeniable realisation. *I can't do this alone. I need help. I have to tell the girls.*

Bridget's three best friends in London were still Mary, Brenda, and Teresa. From the moment she'd met them as an eighteen-year-old, they'd formed a special bond. She knew she could trust them with any *normal* secret. But she feared how they'd react to something like this.

She invited the three girls to her dorm to utter the words she hadn't yet said aloud. Bridget sat at the head of the bed, Mary and

Brenda sat cross-legged alongside her, and Teresa was sprawled out on the carpet. All three were wide-eyed and focused solely on Bridget. She opened her mouth, but nothing came out. Mary, Brenda, and Teresa were all grinning. They looked to be on the verge of giggling, like schoolgirls waiting to be filled in on the latest playground gossip.

'So ...' Bridget said, her voice soft and crumbling. 'I s'pose you're wondering what I hafta tell ya.'

'You're gettin' married!' Teresa wildly guessed.

Bridget shook her head.

'You're moving back to Ireland?' Mary asked.

'Oh, I know!' Brenda said. 'You've got a new boyfriend.'

'No, it's not that,' Bridget said. 'It's ... well ... Jesus ... the thing is, I'm ... ah ...' She couldn't say it. She burst into tears and buried her face in her palms. A moment later, she finally spat it out: 'I'm pregnant.'

Bridget heard the words out loud as she spoke them, but it felt as though they hadn't come from her mouth. She couldn't bring herself to look up at the girls. *How ashamed they must be.* She suddenly felt the warm touch of an arm around her, then a second arm, then the breath of someone on her neck. The three girls were gathered around, embracing her in a group hug.

'It's okay,' Teresa said as she brushed hair out of Bridget's eyes. 'We're here for ye.'

'I just don't know what to do,' Bridget said, finally lifting her head from her hands and facing the girls.

'How far along are you?' Mary asked.

'I'm not sure exactly,' Bridget said. 'But I can't have more than a few months to go.'

The girls' jaws collectively dropped.

'Jaysus, Bridget,' Teresa said. 'How on earth did ye do it? It must be feckin' hard to keep a secret when it's inside ye ... or even worse, sticking outta ye.'

The girls' eyes darted towards Bridget's belly, which was concealed under her loose white frilly top. Teresa reached her hands out towards Bridget's stomach, like a priest blessing a parishioner. 'Do ye mind, Bridget?' she asked.

Bridget shook her head. Teresa's hands pressed against her stomach, softly cupping the concealed bulge.

'Oh my,' Teresa said. 'Can ye believe it? There's a little life inside there. It can probably hear us talkin' right now.'

'It must be thinking "Aren't I lucky to have so many women in my life?",' Brenda said as she also pressed her fingers against Bridget's stomach.

'C'mon, we don't want to scare the poor wee thing,' Mary said. 'Alright, give me a feel.'

As their hands touched Bridget's protruding stomach, just inches from her unborn child, she didn't quite know what to do with herself. She'd spent so long being afraid of what was happening within her that she'd never really entertained the idea of being excited by it.

'Have you thought of names?' Teresa asked.

'I haven't really thought about anything, to be honest,' Bridget admitted.

'Don't worry,' Mary said. 'We'll come up with a plan.'

They sat quietly for a moment, but a plan didn't magically appear. Teresa eventually broke the silence. 'What about Amir?' she asked.

Bridget felt anxious at the very mention of his name. 'He doesn't know,' she said. 'He'll never let me go if he finds out. He can't know.'

'Well, feck him!' Teresa replied. 'The eejit doesn't need to know then.'

'We can do this together,' Brenda said.

'What do ya mean?' Bridget asked.

Brenda got to her feet and started pacing around the room, apparently deep in thought. '*We* can help you,' she said.

Teresa jumped to her feet and joined Brenda. 'We'll be the aunties!' she said, her grin brimming wide, revealing pearly white teeth.

'What about your parents?' Mary asked, in a fashion far more sensible than the other two.

'I haven't told them,' Bridget said. 'But I'm sure they know.'

The girls' grins disappeared.

'Mammy and Daddy have *other* plans for me,' she continued. 'They want the baby to be taken away and raised by my aunt.'

There was a brief silence before it was broken by Teresa, whose cheek muscles were twitching with rage. 'Feckin' Irish pride!' she said. 'I'm tellin' ya. I've seen it all before back home. They treat the poor pregnant girls like skanks, not even worthy of the steam off their piss. They tell 'em to pray for their souls and hope the Lord' – she looked up to the heavens mockingly – 'shows forgiveness for committing such *mortal sins.* Then they cover the whole thing up ... send the child off to the Christian Brothers, or the Sisters ... or they just pretend the child belongs to the grandparents. Bastards. The lotta them!'

Bridget sighed. This burden had followed her around for seven months, but she didn't want it to become the girls' problem as well.

'Are you alright, Bridget?' Mary asked.

'Ah, I'm fine,' she said. 'I was just worried ... you know ...that you lot wouldn't want to be friends with me any more.'

Mary, who was still sitting next to Bridget on the bed, leaned over and wrapped her in a vicelike hug. 'Don't be daft,' she said. 'Of course, we're still friends. Ye haven't done anything wrong.'

Mary's words came as something of a shock to Bridget. She'd spent months thinking she had, in fact, done something wrong – something so bad it would bring shame upon the entire family, something so bad that even a lifetime of Sundays kneeling in church spitting out rosaries wouldn't be enough to absolve it, something so bad it was as though she'd hammered the nails into Jesus Christ himself before he was hung from the cross.

'Of course!' Teresa said. 'Don't ye be carryin' on by saying things like that, Bridget. Course we're here for ye. We can help look after the baby. It'll be no bother compared to some of the shites we deal with on the wards.'

'You're lovely,' Bridget said. 'But I don't want to make this your problem as well.'

'It won't be a problem,' Brenda said. 'We can all go in turns looking after the baby when we're not working.'

'And we'll need our own place as well,' Teresa said. 'We can get an apartment and the little one can have its own room.'

'It?' Brenda said. 'What is it, by the way, Bridget? Are we getting a niece or a nephew?'

'I'm not sure,' Bridget said.

Teresa stared at Bridget's pregnant stomach, her eyes narrowing as though she would suddenly be able to magically see the baby within. 'It's a boy! I know it.'

Brenda followed Teresa's lead and shot a piercing look at Bridget's stomach. 'Hmm. I'm going with a girl. At least then we can buy her pretty things.'

''Twould be nice,' Bridget said. 'But at the moment, I'm more worried about not being able to buy *anything* for the child.'

The room went quiet again. The four of them looked deflated.

'Well,' Mary, the supposedly sensible one, said. 'If we can't afford our own place, maybe the baby can stay here.'

Brenda's and Teresa's faces lit up. 'Oh Lord yes!' Teresa said. 'Think about it. There would always be someone around to look after the baby.'

'And we can spoil the little thing rotten,' Brenda added.

'Jesus, Mary, and Joseph,' Bridget said. 'Think about what the matron would do if she found out.'

'The oul bitch won't know,' Teresa said. 'It'll only be a wee little thing. Sure, no one will see it in here, anyway.'

Teresa, Mary, and Brenda were all staring at Bridget again, as though waiting for her to give the thumbs up to their plan. Her entire body was tingling with nerves. Or maybe it was excitement. She couldn't quite tell.

'Stuff it,' she said. 'Let's do it.'

And so the four young single nurses went back to their rooms that night, believing their plan to raise a child in secret in the dorms of St Ann's General Hospital (with barely a penny to their names and with no idea about being a mother) would actually work. Bridget's inner voice of reason was shouting out *we can't do this*. But she ignored it, for the girls had given her something back that had abandoned her long ago. Hope.

She felt lighter when she went to bed that night. The tightness in her chest that had become so familiar over the previous months had eased. She didn't toss and turn for hours as the moonlight crept further into her room. She didn't lie awake, staring at the ceiling and praying for relief. She simply drifted off, peacefully, and had the best sleep she'd had in months. She woke with a wrenching feeling at the top of her stomach. It was the same wrenching feeling that hit most mornings. But on this morning, as she stumbled to the bathroom across the creaky floorboards, the sickness didn't seem quite so bad. Because she was thinking about the plan that the girls had come up with, and with it came a single yet seemingly unstoppable thought – *maybe this is possible.*

Another month went by, with Bridget growing – not up but out. She got through every day, convincing herself their plan would work. Brenda, Mary, and Teresa took it in turns staying in her room at night. They'd lay blankets and pillows on the floor and sleep on top of it so Bridget and the baby within her could have the single bed to themselves. The girls would always ask, 'Are ye okay, Bridget? Are ye sick, Bridget? Can I get ye a bucket, Bridget? Or some water? How's the baby feeling, Bridget? Is it kicking? Can I feel it?'

By now, Bridget was well and truly *showing*, albeit under thick layers of clothing. Every night as she'd sit in the common room at the nurses' home after a long shift, she'd feel the baby getting restless. Kicking, turning, rolling, poking – it was becoming more fidgety by the day, as though knowing its time to come out was getting closer. Bridget feared if the other girls in the room looked closely enough, they'd be able to see the movement in her belly. But no one ever seemed to notice. The other nurses just watched TV, drank tea, and gossiped like they always did.

As the days passed and Bridget noticed her body growing, she piled on extra layers of clothing to cover up. By this stage, the string in her nurse's apron was getting awfully short as she had to extend it to cover the increasing bump. But no one in the hospital ever seemed to notice either (they never *said* anything, anyway). Apart from her mammy, daddy, and aunty, the only people in the world who knew about the baby were Mary, Brenda, and Teresa. Bridget was just fine with that. The girls never judged, and that meant the world to her. Their support nourished a growing strength within her, not just to simply carry on and get through each day, but, rather, to plan a future that would give her child the best life possible.

KNOCK. KNOCK. KNOCK. It was just after 8 a.m. on a Saturday morning when the monotonous thud rung through her dorm room door. She sat up abruptly. Brenda was lying among a pile of blankets on the floor. She, too, stirred at the sound of the knocks.

'You're expecting someone?' Brenda whispered.

Bridget shook her head as fear suddenly entered it. *Amir! He's found out.* The door swung open. But it wasn't Amir standing behind it. It was the administration lady for the nurses' home, a steely-eyed middle-aged woman the girls only heard from when they'd done something wrong or when there was a problem of some sort. She looked at Bridget in the bed, who had pulled the covers up, stopping just below her eyes. She then looked down at Brenda, who was still stretched out on the floor.

'What are you doing in here?' the admin lady barked at her.

Brenda took a moment to answer. 'I ah ... um ... it's my day off,' she said. 'So I thought I'd come and keep Bridget company.'

'Hmm,' the admin lady mumbled before turning her focus back to Bridget in the bed. 'And *you*. Are you okay?' She didn't ask this in an empathetic way. It was said more in a matter-of-fact, tell-me-what's-going-on-here sort of way.

Bridget nodded.

'Well, the matron wants to see you. Get up and get ready.' The admin lady then turned back to Brenda. 'And *you* ... one person per dorm. No sleeping on floors. If I see you in here again, there'll be hell to pay.'

Bridget was in the matron's office less than fifteen minutes later.

'Sit down,' the matron said.

Bridget obliged, pulling the chair back and sitting, all the while keeping her hands in front of her stomach, her fingers stretched out as though trying to cover as much of the bulge as possible. The matron was a stern woman in her fifties, her face covered in wrinkles, her back hunched, most likely from her early days of heavy lifting as a young nurse. The matron spent most of her time walking around the hospital with her hands behind her back, barking orders at the nurses in between politely greeting patients and their families. But for a nurse to be called in to the matron's office – that was a big deal. Especially when one was told to sit down while in her office.

'We're aware of your *situation,* Nurse Reilly,' the matron said. 'But we have a plan for you. You still have paid holidays owing. So you're going to use that time now. You'll just go on a little holiday. That's all.'

Bridget stared at her feet as the matron addressed her.

'But you'll still receive your wages, Nurse Reilly. You don't need to be worrying about that. There will be a job waiting here for you when you get back. But for now ... there's a place just outside of London. The arrangements have already been made.'

Bridget could feel tears welling in her eyes. She clenched her teeth together and tried to hold them back. She wanted to stand up and tell the matron that she didn't need to go to a place outside of London because her friends had already come up with a plan. And it wouldn't affect any of the other nurses because the baby would be small and out of sight, but well looked after and showered with love and gifts and anything they could afford. So whatever arrangements had been made, they needed to be unmade. Bridget wanted to say all of that, but she didn't. She couldn't. She just sat quietly and gently nodded as the matron went on.

'And when the time comes ... which, by the look of you, can't be too far away ... the child will be taken care of. And you'll be free to return to St Ann's ... and put this mess behind you.'

And just like that, the girls' plan was over. Bridget was destined to leave St Ann's. She would be alone again, and the girls would not be able to save her. The baby was coming in less than a month. Hope had abandoned her.

CHAPTER SEVEN

THE MOTHER AND BABY HOME

Sharon Kennedy was just fifteen when she lost her virginity to a red-headed boy she'd met at the local dance hall. A few months later she went to see the doctor to find out why her period had stopped coming. All the blood seemed to vanish from her face when the doctor told her the news.

'Yep!' the doctor said. 'You've got a bun in your oven, that's for sure. But ah ... there are *ways* you can deal with this. I've seen many a poor woman over the years who's sadly lost the child within them after a nasty fall down the stairs. Devastated they were. The poor women. Their babies didn't stand a chance. Life is precious, you know ... because that's all it takes. A silly trip down the stairs ... and the baby is gone.'

The next day, Sharon stood atop the staircase of her family home, peering down at the floor below. Her eyes scanned the wooden boards on each of the steps before she closed them and leaned forward, balancing precariously on the edge. Suddenly, the front door of the house swung open and her mother walked in, calling for help to bring in bags of shopping.

Sharon confided in her friends at school: two girls she'd been close to for as long as she could remember. The girls told her about a trick they'd heard that could solve her problem.

'Gin,' one friend said. 'Drink as much as you can stomach. And a hot bath. Hotter the better. I've heard that'll do it.'

After school, Sharon went to the corner store, found a bottle of gin, and hid it in her jacket pocket. It was the first time she'd ever stolen anything. She went home and drew a hot bath. Clasping the gin, she read the back of the bottle, trying to figure out how much she would need to drink to get the job done. She took a swig from the bottle, scrunching her face as the foul burning taste passed over her tongue and down her throat. She forced another sip into her mouth, then began retching. She threw up into the bath. Remnants of gin and stomach acid floated on top of the water. But still, Sharon stepped into it, lowering her body until every part of her from the neck down was below the surface.

For a month or so, Sharon did the same thing every night – gulping down gin before jumping into a searing hot bath. But her period didn't return. So she again went to her friends for help.

'There's another way,' one of her friends said. 'Not as nice as the other trick. But I heard about someone who did it. My cousin knew her. And it worked. All you need to do is find a leech. Any old leech will do. And then ... you know ... you put it ... up there. Not nice, I know. But still ... better than being disowned.'

Sharon walked down to a stream near her family home after school. She searched for hours before finally finding a leech on the bank. She put the squirming little creature in her pocket and went straight home, heading into her room and closing the door.

She held the leech under the ceiling light, examining it. The shiny black slug was wriggling, trying to latch on to Sharon's soft fingers. Her hands were trembling, just like her grandmother's hands used to tremble before she had died several years earlier. She held the leech for so long, it managed to suck on to her. Blood seeped from her finger as the leech slowly filled itself. She gasped, throwing it onto the floor and squashing it with her shoe.

Telling her parents was now the only option. Her mother and father sat still and refused to look at her when she told them the news. Her father, an Irishman who'd moved to England for work in his teens, eventually said, 'Tis only one thing to do. We'll see Father Barry and he'll sort it. And then when the time gets close, ye'll go away and have it dealt with. Father Barry will be able to get ye into one of them places. Then, when it's done … that'll be it. You come back and we'll leave the unpleasantness behind us. Or … Lord help us … don't bother coming back at all.'

Sharon was sent to a mother and baby home in Epping, hundreds of miles away from her family house. Her parents insisted she wear a fake wedding ring on the journey down there. And she was booked in under the name Worthington instead of Kennedy so people would assume it was her married name. Sharon continued her studies at the mother and baby home until the baby came. And then, six weeks later, after adoptive parents were found, Sharon returned to her family, pledging to never talk of it again.

Catherine Sloane had just turned twenty when she fell pregnant in Dublin. The first person she told was her boyfriend of three months – a young postman she was madly in love with.

'You whore!' was how he responded to the news. 'You been feckin' sleepin' round on me. Yeer nothin' but an oul slut. Get outta me sight!'

He didn't hit her. But Catherine thought he might have if she'd stayed in his sight much longer.

With her boyfriend no longer in the picture, Catherine turned to her parents for help.

'Course no man would want to marry ye,' her mother said. 'When you've doomed a child to eternity in hell ... who could blame the lad for not wanting anythin' to do with ya?'

Months later, Catherine was told by her boss that she would not have a job to return to after the birth because 'Receptionists at this office should be nice, good Catholics, *not* prostitute types. I'm sure you could find work at a brothel, Miss Sloane ... That'd be more fitting for your type. Lord above, yeer poor family! How beside themselves they must be.'

She was sent to a mother and baby home in England (which had been organised by their local parish priest in Ireland), just in case someone in Dublin who knew the family found out she was pregnant. At the home, Catherine told her social worker that she was going to keep the baby after it was born.

'Not to worry. I'll get a job and look after the child all by me'self. I'll write to every office in London if I have to. It'll be grand. Just the two of us. I don't need me mammy or daddy or no feckin' boy to help me. I'm never going back to Ireland anyway. All I need is me little one.' Catherine clasped her hands to her stomach, gently and lovingly cupping the bulge.

The social worker revealed Catherine's plans to the Reverend Mother at the home, who in turn spoke to the matron at the local hospital. They all agreed that Catherine's 'absurd' plan had to be put to a stop.

Catherine eventually gave birth to a little girl. She heard her screams for the first time as she was cleaned up by the midwives. She then watched from her hospital bed as her little girl was carried out of the room, before she even had a chance to hold her. With nowhere else to go, Catherine was sent back to the mother and baby home, where she was allowed to stay for six weeks after the birth. Unlike other unmarried mothers at the home, Catherine was forbidden from seeing or holding her little girl during that time, even though she was just next door in the nursery. The Reverend Mother told Catherine she was being selfish and childish for even suggesting she could keep the baby as her own, especially when she was not yet twenty-one and therefore still a child herself.

With just chores to fill her time, Catherine scrubbed, dusted, swept, and mopped her way through six weeks at the home. But every night, after all the girls and nuns had fallen asleep, she snuck into the corridor next to the nursery. And there in the darkness, with just the glow of the moonlight coming through the window, she'd stare at her little girl as she slept in the crib. Catherine would press her hands up against the glass that divided the nursery and corridor and simply watch with a smile as her daughter took baby breaths in and out in her apparent peaceful slumber.

But one night, Catherine discovered her daughter's crib was empty. She looked throughout the entire nursery, but her little girl was nowhere to be seen. Catherine dropped to the floor outside the nursery and sobbed all night until the sun came up. She was never seen at the home again.

Louise Taylor lived with her parents in London, where she was studying to become a teacher. She was nineteen when she met a young man at a college party. They had a fling. It was fun at first, maybe because it was all new and exciting to Louise. Or maybe it was fun because she was drunk whenever she saw him and couldn't think straight. Whatever it was, it wore off after several encounters. Louise told the young man that she had no interest in seeing him any more. But he refused to listen. He held her down, covering her mouth with his hand to muffle her screams. And then he raped her.

A month later, Louise found out she was pregnant. Distraught and in shock, she went to her parents for help.

'Well, there's the honourable thing to do,' her father said. 'If you want the kid to be legitimate, you need to marry this bloke.'

'No!' Louise screamed. 'I'm never seeing him again.'

She refused to leave the house for days. She cried herself to sleep every night and hid under the covers in the mornings when her mother tried to pull her out of bed so she could attend her classes at college. One afternoon, Louise took a handful of sleeping tablets she found in her parents' drawer. Her mother later found her frothing at the mouth, rolling all over the floor. The doctors were able to pump her stomach in time to save her life. Louise's mother took her to their local priest, who appeared surprised to see them, considering they'd been absent from church for many years. The priest prescribed Louise three rosaries to deal with her troubles and arranged for her to be put into a mother and baby home just outside London in a place called Epping.

Louise kept to herself at the mother and baby home. She barely spoke to the other girls, and when she did, she certainly didn't mention anything about pregnancy or babies or marriage or boys of any kind. Her father refused to visit her in the weeks before the birth. Her mother, however, did drop by every Saturday morning. She'd take Louise into town, where they'd shop or go to the cinema. At the end of every visit, Louise would tell her mother, 'I just want this thing out of me. I want to pretend all of this never happened.'

Louise eventually gave birth to a little boy. She had him right in the mother and baby home – by the time the nuns had realised she was fully dilated, it was too late to take her to the local hospital.

Her mother continued to visit her at the home after the child was born, but she refused to see her grandson or even walk past the nursery. Louise told her mother, 'I thought I'd see *him* when I look at his little face. But I don't. I just see ... my beautiful boy.'

Louise began joining some of the other mothers at the home, who knitted little jumpers and beanies for their babies. She spent her days cuddling him in between her regular chores. And she cried every night when she was kicked out of the nursery and forced to leave her boy alone. But she got out of bed spritely the next morning, when she was allowed back in to see him again. Six weeks passed, but Louise's social worker had still not found adoptive parents for her child.

'It's terribly hard,' the social worker said. 'What with all the little ones who need homes around the country. But I must say, it's especially hard when a child is of mixed race, like your one. Boys tend to be less desirable as well. People want little white girls. NOT little *brown boys*, like yours.'

Louise's baby was taken away to an orphanage, where he stayed for another month until adoptive parents were finally found. Louise was called in to the adoption agency on the outskirts of London to sign the papers and make the handover official. It would be her final chance to say goodbye to her son. She was taken into a small room at the agency, where she was given two minutes alone with her child. She was lucky to get this chance, she was told. Her tears sprinkled him as she hugged him for the final time. He was then carried away by the social worker into the next room, where he was presumably handed over to his new parents. Louise could hear his screams through the wall, after he was taken away. She screamed too and fell to the ground, smashing her fists on the cold concrete floor. Staff at the adoption agency had to put a needle in her to calm her down.

Louise, Catherine, and Sharon never met each other. But each of them shared a bond that would remain for life. They were all bound by the same pain, the same misery. And they all attended the same mother and baby home in Epping, just outside of London. That's where they lived before the births of their children, and then for six weeks afterwards. And now Bridget Reilly, alone and eight months pregnant, was on the train on the way to Epping, where she too was destined to become bound by the same pain and misery as Louise, Catherine, and Sharon.

Rain drizzled on Bridget as she stood at the front gates of the mother and baby home, her hands pressed against her belly, which was hidden underneath her thick duffel coat. The building in front of her was two storeys of dull grey brick with a large cross perched upon its roof. It was surrounded by a stone wall, which was high enough to stop prying eyes from looking into the grounds. The first thing she saw when she emerged through the front door was a grand staircase. Light shone off its banister as though it had been freshly polished. Its wooden steps were dust-free and glossy and also looked like they had recently been cleaned. An old nun appeared at the top of the staircase. Bridget assumed this must be the Reverend Mother – the nun who ruled the roost. Only her wrinkled, sour face was visible within her crisp white wimble (the traditional headpiece worn by nuns). Her black garments dragged along the steps as she walked down them towards the front entrance. She stopped in front of Bridget, who was trembling, and looked her up and down through narrowed black beady eyes.

'See these stairs,' the Reverend Mother said. 'The only time you are to be seen on them is if you are cleaning them. These stairs are only for guests. You, *Miss*, like all the other girls, are not a guest. You should just be thanking the Lord you have a proper roof over your head at all. Tis more than Mary and Holy St Joseph were given when baby Jesus was born in Bethlehem. So, while you're here, thank the Lord for how lucky you are. And do your chores as though the Lord himself is watching over your shoulder. For he is. And so am I, *Miss*. Don't make the mistake of thinking this is a holiday. It's not. Tis your penance.'

Bridget was escorted around the grounds by one of the other unmarried pregnant girls. She was a blonde-haired young woman with a northern English accent. She was about the same age as Bridget, but the bump sticking out of her dress was much bigger, about twice the size of Bridget's, it seemed. The young woman didn't introduce herself by name; she just walked ahead of Bridget and rattled off instructions and advice.

'This is your room,' the young woman said as she led Bridget into a dorm with four single beds in it. 'Make sure you make your bed every morning or the nuns won't be happy! And there's no sleeping in. We have to be up by seven to get everything done before the afternoon. Come, I'll take ya through your chores.'

She took Bridget down a dingy old hallway lined with paintings of the Sacred Heart of Jesus and Mother Mary and other various saints. The smell of bleach-like chemicals rose up from the cold concrete floor as they walked. They came across a heavily pregnant woman on her hands and knees, scrubbing the floor with a steel brush. A thick layer of sweat covered the woman's forehead, her curly brown hair frizzed out in different directions, and her massive belly barely hovered over the surface she was cleaning. Bridget's guide walked past the cleaning woman as though it was a normal thing. Bridget, on the other hand, had to fight the urge to stop and help the poor scrubbing-woman to her feet.

The kitchen was dimly lit with just a single lightbulb hanging from the centre of the ceiling. The black metal stovetop and oven looked like they'd been there for decades (or the equivalent of several thousand illegitimate babies' worth). Two pregnant women were scrubbing them with thick steel brushes. Other girls were peeling and chopping vegetables around a table in the middle of the kitchen.

'This is where you'll be,' Bridget's escort said. 'You cooked before?'

Bridget nodded.

'Good. You'll be doing plenty of it here.'

The young woman then took Bridget down another hallway, past the nursery. Bridget slowed down and peered in through the glass. There were about a dozen cribs in the nursery, a baby in each of them. The sound of their cries carried through the glass and into the hallway.

'You're not allowed in here,' the young woman said. 'Not until you've had it, that is. Then you have to get up at five thirty every morning and feed it. From a bottle ... no breastfeeding allowed.'

Two pregnant women carrying buckets full of coal walked past, their hands and faces blackened as though they'd spent a day working underground in a mine.

'Your back will ache after the first day of the chores,' Bridget's escort said. 'I'd like to say it gets better, but it doesn't. Whatever you do, don't complain to the sisters or the old bitch Reverend Mother. They don't give a toss about your back, or mine for that matter. They don't care if you're about to pop. Shit, they wouldn't care if the baby was half hanging out of you. I heard there was a girl whose water broke on the floor. The nuns made her mop it up before they sent her to the hospital. Can you believe that? All they care about ... is that you do as you're told and don't talk back.'

'Jesus,' Bridget said, soft enough that it was almost under her breath.

'He's not gonna help you neither,' her escort said with a condescending smirk.

The young woman then led Bridget into the common room. 'You're allowed in here after your chores are done.'

Several pregnant girls were sitting in the corner knitting. Two more were playing cards at a table, casually chatting as they puffed away on cigarettes.

'There's no TV, so you have to find other ways to entertain yourself. You got a coat?'

Bridget nodded.

'Good. The sisters won't let you go into town if you don't have one. We're allowed to go shopping and all that. Just make sure you cover up or the Reverend Mother will get all demented and threaten to lock ya up for the rest of your stay. She's a nasty old thing.'

The young woman then took Bridget into the laundry, where

about half a dozen pregnant women were hand-washing clothes in large metal tubs. Steam was rising from a huge rusty boiler, which was spewing out hot air into the crammed, poorly ventilated space. All the women working in here were red-faced and tinged with sweat.

'Lucky you're not in here,' Bridget's escort whispered. 'No one wants the laundry shift. You get a lot more than a sore back working in here.'

Finally, the young woman took Bridget through the grounds outside. They walked along a crumbling footpath among long green grass and large trees that were swaying in the breeze. Bridget thought it would have been a lovely little patch of land in the English countryside, if not for all the unmarried pregnant women doing hard labour. The tour finished when they arrived at the chapel, which was just near the front entrance.

'We have Mass every Sunday,' her escort said. 'There's confession as well. But trust me, Father Mooney knows what your sins are just by looking at ya. I mean, have a look at these fuckin' camel humps sticking out of us ... It's not hard to guess what sinning we did to get ourselves in here.'

The young woman winked at her, then walked away, still not having introduced herself.

Bridget got through her first week in Epping, quickly falling into a regimented daily routine. Every morning she woke at 7 a.m., got dressed, made her bed, and then said a morning prayer with the other girls before breakfast. It was then time to begin her morning chores. She was assigned to peeling spuds in the kitchen, much like she used to when growing up in Belmullet. Her wrists ached as she spent hours every morning filling buckets with potato peelings. The spuds gave off an occasional foul whiff, as though they were on the verge of rotting. But it was nothing a dip in boiling water couldn't fix. After peeling enough to feed twenty women and half a dozen nuns, Bridget's hands were so badly cramped she couldn't outstretch her fingers. But there was no time to rest or recover.

Next, she had to wipe down the benches and clean all the pots and pans and cutlery that had been used throughout the morning. Then it was on to scrubbing the filthy kitchen floor. The skin wore away on her knees and elbows, leaving blotches of red streaked with blood, while sweat dripped from her brow onto the cold concrete. She thought it must have been a funny sight – heavily pregnant women on the verge of popping, doing hard labour. It felt like the home was so old and dilapidated that it needed to be cleaned every day just to stop it from toppling over. But the chores kept Bridget standing as well. It kept her mind occupied on something other than her shame. So, she put her head down and worked, often singing to herself to pass the time.

By early afternoon, her chores were done for the day. She was free to do whatever she liked before dinner at 6 p.m. Some days she stayed at the home and read a book in the common room while other women sat around and drank tea, knitted, and played cards. Other days, she went shopping in town, but not before first covering her bump with her duffel coat. After dinner each night, Bridget lay in bed, sideways on the lumpy mattress, and rested her aching muscles. Every night, without fail, when the lights cut out and the dorm fell into darkness, the soft sounds of women sobbing were all around her.

The girls at the home were allowed visitors in the afternoons. Some of their parents came to see them, even taking them into town for a few hours. There were also a few young men who came to visit. Bridget assumed they were the soon-to-be fathers of the unborn babies. These men had no responsibility to be involved in the child's life. The burden was solely upon the mother. Perhaps that's why so few of the fathers came to visit.

Despite spending most of her waking hours with the other girls at the home, Bridget barely knew anything about them. All she knew was what was grotesquely obvious – they were pregnant with their *first* child. The girls were told they would not be welcome back at the home if they fell pregnant again, without a ring on their finger.

'The naughty girls who don't learn their lesson the first time are no better than prostitutes,' one of the nuns had said one day.

No one was willing to reveal too much about their lives back in the real world. The nuns also told them not to get too close to each other, for they would have to cease all ties when they left the home after giving birth. The less they knew about each other, 'the easier the whole unfortunate and unpleasant experience would be to forget,' the nuns always said.

And while the women all shared the same protruding mark of late-stage pregnancy, none of them ever confided in each other or spoke of their looming labour. Instead, each day they simply focused on the other sort of labour – the sweeping, scrubbing, dusting, and mopping kind. The nuns and the Reverend Mother certainly never told them what to expect in childbirth either. There was no advice, no lessons, no education of any type. Just silence. Bridget wondered if the other girls were just as clueless about childbirth as she was. But she was too scared to speak up and find out. She never saw any of the other girls going into labour. Occasionally, she'd be made to stay in her room as screams rang from another part of the home. Eventually, when she was allowed out of the room, there would be an ambulance exiting through the front gates. The thought of being in the back of one of those ambulances with her child coming out of her weighed on Bridget's mind. She wondered what she'd think, what'd she'd feel in that moment, and whether she'd be able to handle it.

The women who went into labour usually spent a few days in the local hospital before returning to the home with their newborns. They'd be allowed to stay for six more weeks before being sent their separate ways. Bridget didn't see these women in the mornings because they were in the nursery caring for their little ones. But even though they'd just given birth, they weren't excused from doing chores like everyone else. After feeding and bathing their babies, they'd join the pregnant women in cleaning the home from top to bottom. If, for some reason, a woman hadn't properly recovered from the labour and couldn't be on her feet for too long, she would be given chores like sewing or polishing that could be done from bed.

Each woman was assigned a social worker, who took charge of finding adoptive parents for the child. 'It's for the best,' the social workers always said when referring to adoption. Sometimes they visited the home to speak to the women in person and update them on the progress to find parents. But the social workers were so busy with all the illegitimate children being born across the country, they usually dealt with the mothers by phone instead.

One of the older women at the home, Helen O'Hara, was about thirty. Helen spoke with an Irish accent, like many of the other women. And also like the other women, she never revealed too much about her life outside the home. After giving birth, Helen returned from the local hospital with twins.

'Imagine that!' one of the other unmarried mothers said. '*Double* the shame. Twice as much to cover up.'

A few days later, as Bridget was mopping a hallway, she heard a high-pitched scream from Helen's dorm room. She dropped her mop and rushed towards the shrieking sound. She found Helen on her hands and knees next to her bed. One of the babies was on top of the covers; the other child was on the floor, red-faced and howling. Helen was also screaming as she picked up the fallen boy and cradled him in her arms. She rocked him back and forth, trying to calm him, but he wouldn't stop screaming. Bridget rushed to Helen's side, placing a hand on her shoulder.

'He f-f-f-fell off the bed,' Helen sobbed.

'It's okay,' Bridget said. 'Shhh. It's okay.'

Helen's tears flowed far more heavily than the little boy's. A few other girls who must have heard the screams also came into the room to console her. The little boy, burrowed in Helen's arms, didn't appear to have a scratch on him.

'Someone get the Reverend Mother!' one of the girls screamed.

Bridget and the other girls helped Helen to her feet and sat her on the bed with the baby still in her arms. A few minutes later, the Reverend Mother came into the room.

'What have you done?' she said, spit flying.

Helen opened her mouth to speak, but no words came out amid her sobs.

'The baby fell off the bed,' Bridget said.

'Lord above!' the Reverend Mother responded, her wrinkled face turning pink with rage within her habit. 'And what is a child doing in a bed in the first place?'

'I w-was ch-ch-changing them, Reverend Mother,' Helen said.

'Eejit,' the Reverend Mother said, rolling her black beady eyes. 'What did ye expect to happen? Silly girl. A bed is no place for a child. Especially a child that was conceived in sin *on* a bed by its wicked parents.'

'P-please, Reverend Mother. I need to take him to the doctor. He hit his head. P-p-please. Can you call an ambulance?'

'Ambulance?' the Reverend Mother barked back. 'The child looks fine to me. 'Twould be a waste of time for the hard-workin' paramedics of this town, who have better things to be doin' than lookin' after the illegitimate child of a silly girl like you.'

'Please,' Helen pleaded again. 'I'll take a taxi to the hospital myself. I just need money. Can you give me some? Please!'

'Are ye coddin' me?' the Reverend Mother said. 'The child hasn't got a mark on it. Now take that sour puss off ye face and get the pair of them back to the nursery.'

The Reverend Mother turned on her heels and walked back out the way she had come. Bridget and the other girls gathered around Helen and continued to console her. The baby in her arms began to calm down, but Helen did not. Bridget wanted to give the poor woman money for a taxi, but she had none. She was still being paid her measly nurse's wage by St Ann's General Hospital, but she didn't have access to any of it. The money was being held in the care of the nuns at the mother and baby home, which, of course, included the Reverend Mother.

Bridget stayed with Helen for more than an hour until she'd finally calmed down. But when night fell and she lay in her bed, she couldn't stop thinking about the Reverend Mother and how she'd refused to help poor Helen. And with those thoughts came a persistent question that had no reasonable answer accompanying it – *how could a servant of the Lord be so heartless?*

CHAPTER EIGHT

IT'S TIME

I t began as an aching stomach – a cramp, just like any Bridget had felt before. It first hit just after breakfast as she was peeling the first potato of the morning. She hunched over, hands on knees, and took a deep breath, riding it out. The ache abruptly faded away to nothingness, and she didn't give it another thought. Until it hit again, later in the morning. She was scrubbing grease off the stovetop when she felt it straining away in her gut. It lasted about a minute before it subsided once more. *It's just a sore stomach.*

She got on with her day, finishing her chores and then relaxing in the common room, where she read a book. The cramps continued to come and go as the day went on. By dinner time, they were coming every half hour or so. They arrived with a certain consistency and rhythm, like a set of waves rolling in from deeper waters and crashing along the shore. By dinner, the pain was far greater than it had been at the start of the day, but it was still bearable. Bridget was able to sit among the other girls at dinner without drawing attention to herself. She went straight to her dorm after dinner and tucked herself beneath the sheets, which she'd neatly tucked over her mattress that morning. *It's just a stomach ache,* she kept telling herself as she buried her head in the pillow, clenching her teeth and waiting for respite to come. And it did; every fifteen minutes or so, sweet relief came upon her as the wave of discomfort washed away.

But as the evening went on, the tightening of her abdomen, the twisting and squeezing in her stomach, grew more intense with every surge. It even spread into her back and throughout the rest of her torso. The stillness in between the bursts of pain was getting shorter every time. But *time* itself became lost on her. She had no idea how long she'd been in bed since dinner. *Hail Mary, full of grace. Our Lord is with thee ...* she prayed as the sensation struck her again ... *blessed art though among women, and blessed is the fruit of thy womb, Jesus ...* This burst had a far more vicious bite than anything she'd experienced already. *Holy Mary, mother of God. Pray for us sinners...* she gasped, clenching her pillow and burying her face further into it. *Now and at the hour of our death. Amen.*

As though on cue, the sensation within her retreated. She lifted her head from the pillow, which was damp with sweat. Her roommates were standing over the bed, looking down through wide eyes. She shared a room with three young women who were also in the final days of their pregnancy. And like most of the women at the home, she barely knew anything about them.

'Are you alright?' one of the women asked.

'Oh, I'm grand,' Bridget said. 'Just a sore tummy.'

The girls didn't look convinced, but they went back to their beds anyway.

The pain kept coming as the darkness of night spread into the room. Each wave was longer and stronger than the last, and closer to the onslaught of the next one. That morning it had been a bearable swell in otherwise still waters, but now the waters were choppy, the crashing seas creating a mountainous explosion of whitewash that would swallow anything in its path. And Bridget was in the midst of it, struggling to stay afloat with no solid ground beneath her feet. Every time it came, she scrunched her eyes as tight as she could, trying to get lost in the black abyss at the back of her lids. Her roommates must have noticed it was getting worse, because they turned the light on and surrounded her bed again.

'I'm fine, girls,' she tried to reassure them. 'It's fine.'

'Someone get the Reverend Mother,' one of the girls yelled.

Bridget tried to look calm. *Don't let them see your pain.* She kept telling herself that, as though the feeling within her was something to be ashamed of. The girls standing over her were ghostly pale and appeared to be trembling.

'I'm fine,' Bridget said again. 'You can go back to bed.'

She closed her eyes. And when she opened them, the Reverend Mother was in the room, peering down at her.

'Tell me what's wrong with you,' the Reverend Mother said.

Bridget inhaled but couldn't draw enough breath to produce words as she felt another wave crashing within. The Reverend Mother turned to Bridget's roommates. ''Twill be enough for tonight,' she spat at them. 'Back to bed. All of ye!'

She turned around and left the room, her black garments flapping outward like a curtain in the breeze.

'It's okay, girls,' Bridget said. 'You can turn the lights out now. Please, just go to sleep.'

The evening dragged on, heavily and slowly, edging towards midnight. The pain was now coming on every five minutes or so, grinding Bridget down a bit further every time it hit. Her roommates refused to let her be. They gathered around her bed, one of them holding her hand, another wiping her forehead, and another saying everything would be okay. She kept telling herself, *Don't let them see. Don't let them see. Don't let them see.* She didn't want the girls to worry. But mainly she didn't want them to *see* the pain that was awaiting them.

She wasn't sure how much time passed before one of the girls said, 'That's it! I'm going to get the old bitch again!'

The Reverend Mother barged into the room several minutes later. Her dark eyes narrowed as she glared at Bridget, before turning back to a younger nun who was standing in the doorway. 'Call an ambulance,' the Reverend Mother said. 'The baby is coming.'

Several contractions later, the ambulance arrived. Bridget was loaded in the back. As the rear doors slammed shut, it cut out her final glimpse of the Reverend Mother, who was standing on the front steps of the home, glaring ahead coldly, her black garments flailing in the wind. The rocks on the driveway made a crackling sound as the wheels rolled over them. Red lights flashed and the siren blared as the ambulance set off along the winding country roads towards the local hospital. A young paramedic, probably in his early twenties, was sitting beside Bridget in the back of the ambulance, while another young man, not much older, sat up front behind the wheel and handled the narrow bends.

'Breathe, Bridget,' the young paramedic in the back said. 'Slow, deep breaths.'

Every three minutes or so, the wave returned. It now felt as though her internal organs were being slowly squeezed. One minute of agony, three minutes of relief; one minute of agony, three minutes of relief; … on and on it went.

'It's okay,' the paramedic kept saying. 'Remember, breathe. Nice and slow. We're not far away from the hospital.' He grabbed Bridget's trembling hand and squeezed it. 'You're doing so well,' he said, smiling at her as the ambulance zoomed through the countryside, throwing out flashing red light into the midnight darkness.

She tried to stay calm. But she was terrified; she had no idea what she was about to go through. Her mind shifted to her mammy, who had been through this seven times before (one child, Willy, had sadly died as an infant). Bridget would have given anything for her mammy to be there in the ambulance with her, holding her hand and telling her everything would be alright. But she knew it was a futile thought. The person holding her hand and reassuring her was, in fact, a stranger. A young man whose name she didn't even know, a paramedic simply doing his job. But as the ambulance swerved back and forth, side to side, and up and down over the potholes and uneven surface as it traversed along the winding roads towards Epping Hospital, that young man at Bridget's side was so much more than just a stranger who was simply doing his job. He was as much a hero to her as anyone had ever been.

'Good, Bridget. Stay calm. Slow breaths and ride it out. Good girl. We're not far away.' The paramedic kept saying that: 'We're not far away.' But Bridget felt as though the journey would never end. That is until finally, after who knows how long, the siren cut out and the wheels slowed to a stop.

'We're here, Bridget,' the paramedic said.

The two young men wheeled her out the back of the ambulance, then up the ramp and through the front doors of the hospital. She wanted to thank them. But she was so focused on her breathing, she feared speaking might disrupt the flow.

'You're doing well,' the paramedic kept whispering in her ear as he wheeled her through the hospital. She lay back on the gurney, observing the fluorescent ceiling lights she was passing beneath. The sterile smell of cleaning products emanating from the floor reminded her of her days working on the wards of St Ann's in London. The gurney came to a stop, and a woman's face appeared above Bridget. She was in her forties and wearing a blue uniform and white nurse's hat. Beads of sweat clung to the nurse's forehead, and she was panting like she'd run halfway around the hospital to be here. Bridget assumed this must be the midwife.

'Eight centimetres,' the young paramedic said to her.

The paramedics and midwife spoke among themselves for a few minutes. Bridget couldn't hear what they were saying. But she wasn't trying to listen in, either. Her only focus was the latest wave of pain, which she was struggling to ride out. By the time it eased, the midwife had finished talking with the paramedics and turned her attention towards her.

'Okay, Miss Reilly,' the midwife said. 'Your baby's picked a busy night to come. There're a few women who are ahead of you at the moment. I'm going to get these nice young men to take you into a room. You'll need to wait in there for a little while by yourself, then we'll be in to get you.'

The midwife took off hurriedly through the hospital doors, while the paramedics wheeled Bridget into a private room. They then carefully helped her from the gurney and onto the hospital bed.

'We have to leave you now,' said the young paramedic who had sat with her in the back of the ambulance. 'Don't worry, Bridget. The midwife won't be long. Remember, keep breathing, slow and deep. Won't be long now. You can do this.'

He squeezed her hand again, one final time, and left the room. Bridget squirmed around in the bed, trying to get comfortable as the painful wave rolled in once more. But no matter what position she moved into, it wouldn't relent. She desperately wanted the paramedic to return so he could squeeze her hand again and tell her everything would be okay. But the echoes of his footsteps from the outside corridor had disappeared. He was gone, and she was all alone.

Please, Lord, forgive me for my sins. Give me strength, Lord. I can't do this alone. Look over the child, protect the child, keep them safe. Please! she prayed as time passed. Again, her concept of time was lost. But it may have been half an hour or so before the midwife burst into the room, a glint of sweat still upon her face, specks of blood and other unknown stains on her blouse. She examined between Bridget's legs.

'That looks to me like ten centimetres,' she said. 'You're ready, Miss Reilly.'

Two young nurses, no older than twenty-one, joined them in the room.

'Come on,' the midwife ordered her junior colleagues. 'Nice and quickly now. Get those wheels moving. Miss Reilly's not going to push herself to the delivery room.'

The two young nurses did as they were told and manoeuvred the bed through the door and down the corridor.

'Don't look so scared,' one of the young nurses said to Bridget in an Irish accent. 'Ye'll be 'right.'

'Course ye will,' the other young nurse said, also with the unmistakeable twang of Irish-ness.

Bridget looked up at the two young nurses, who were no doubt learning their craft in the chaos of the hospital. Not that long ago, she had been just like them – young and innocent, a young nurse with a bright future. But now the tables were turned. She wasn't the one caring for patients; she was the one *in* the hospital bed, in need of care.

Within a few minutes they were in the delivery room. The young nurses were standing either side of her while the midwife was examining her from below.

'You'll feel the urge to push,' the midwife said. 'Listen to me and push when I tell you to push, ease up when I tell you to ease up, and breathe when I tell you to breathe. Do that and everything will be fine, dear.'

A thick layer of sweat had formed on Bridget's brow and was trickling down her nose and over her eyes. The midwife, whose brow was also sweaty, noticed and moved to the head of the bed, dabbing Bridget's face with a cloth.

'Get her legs in the stirrups, girls,' the midwife ordered.

The young Irish nurses moved the stirrups into position and fastened Bridget's feet into them. Sweat had already reappeared on her forehead, but the midwife was quick to wipe it away. The midwife then handed the cloth to one of the young Irish nurses and returned to the foot of the bed.

'The hard part's over,' the midwife said. 'Think of it like this – each push is two steps forward, one step back. Got it? Two steps forward, one step back.'

Bridget nodded as the midwife continued to address her.

'When I tell you to push, I want you to give me one nice big push, just like you would on the toilet. Okay, when I tell you.'

Another contraction stirred within Bridget.

'Push!' the midwife ordered.

Bridget gritted her teeth, clenching every muscle in her body and pushing with all her might.

'Again. Push!' the midwife said.

She felt the urge to scream, but she kept it within. *Don't let them hear your pain.*

'One more. Push!'

Bridget exhaled, a big gasping breath that darkened her vision around the edges and turned her face a bright shade of red.

'And ... relax!' the midwife finally said. 'Good start. Rest now before the next one comes. Slow, deep breaths while you wait. Good girl. You were made for this.'

On and on it went. One push at a time. Although *time* didn't exist for Bridget any more. Her life was now being measured in pushes. Each push was a step closer to relief, a step closer to motherhood. The young nurses were clenching her hands, one on either side, while one of them continued wiping sweat from her forehead.

'I see the head,' the midwife eventually announced. 'Okay, ready ... push!'

Overwhelming sensations of burning, stinging, and stretching accompanied every push.

'Stop for a moment, Miss Reilly,' the midwife said. 'Not too fast now, we don't want you to tear. Okay, when I tell you ... ready ... and push! There's the forehead ... push... the nose is out. I see the mouth and the chin. Push ... That's it! The head's out!'

The midwife applied suction to the baby's head. Bridget fell back into the bed, trying to catch her breath the way a sprinter does when they've just run a hundred-metre dash.

'Rest now for a moment,' the midwife said.

But it barely felt like a moment had passed before she spoke again.

'We're almost there. Ready to push again, Miss Reilly. So close now. When I tell you ... here we go ... one, two, three, push!

There's one shoulder ... and there's the other. Just one more, you're almost there. On my word. One, two, three, *push*!'

Bridget harnessed every bit of energy into that one final push. The pressure, the burning, the aching, the excruciating agony soared again, one final time. And then it came to a sudden halt. Just like that, she wasn't hurting any more. She fell back into the hospital bed, panting heavily, utterly exhausted.

'It's a girl,' the midwife announced, cradling the newborn in her arms.

Silence spread through the room, becoming a lingering stillness. It was eerily quiet – *too* quiet for *too* long.

'She's not crying!' Bridget called out.

Her vision blurred as tears filled her eyes. And still that unnerving, unwelcome silence hung about.

'What's wrong?' she asked again, a shrill panic in her voice. But the midwife said nothing as she examined the baby at a nearby table. The silence did all the talking. It devoured the breath right out of Bridget. Fear took hold of her. And she knew if that dreaded silence carried on any longer, she would have to break it herself – with her own screams.

'What is it?' she asked again. 'Is she *alright*?'

And then, right on cue, her little girl started to cry. The ear-splitting shriek of new life filled the hospital room. It was the sweetest sound Bridget had ever heard – far sweeter than the greatest fiddle players in Ireland. It was even sweeter than her father's angelic singing voice. This sound, her daughter's first cries, were jagged squeals so high-pitched, you'd think they could shatter glass. They were sharp and rusty, piercing into Bridget's ears with a barrelling intensity. In any other moment, it might have been a disturbing sound – a cry for help, a cry of uncertainty, a cry of fear. But in this hospital, in this room, at this moment, it was the beautiful sound of a starting life: a life Bridget had created.

The midwife carried the baby away towards a glass crib, where the young nurses started cleaning her up. Bridget's body felt wrecked, almost void of energy. But she still had enough strength to lift her head to peek at her little girl.

'Is her nose alright?' she asked, noticing a strange protrusion in the middle of her little girl's face.

The young Irish nurses laughed. 'Ah, her nose is grand,' one of them said. 'Just looks strange through the glass is all.'

'So she's okay?' Bridget asked again, apprehensively.

'Don't ye be worrying. She's a wee gem.'

The doors of the room swung open and the thuds of a heavy-footed person approached. It was a doctor, an Englishman in his late twenties, just his brown eyes visible between his blue mask and cap. He stopped at the end of Bridget's bed, pulling his plastic gloves over his outstretched fingers. A piercing sensation suddenly hit Bridget below. She looked down but could only see the top of the doctor's blue hospital cap. He was stitching her up, without so much as a warning. It was the first time she realised she had torn during the delivery. She winced every time the needle went through her tender skin. But she stayed silent and turned her gaze towards her little girl in the glass crib. A few minutes later, another doctor came into the room. He was about ten years older than the other doctor. The older physician was a tall, barrel-chested man with bronzed skin and sandy-blond hair. He spoke to Bridget in a distinctively Australian accent.

'How are ya feeling, Miss Reilly?' he asked.

'I'm grand now, doctor,' she said.

The Aussie doctor turned to his junior colleague. 'She looks anaemic.' He nudged the younger doctor aside and took over the stitching. 'Miss Reilly, I'm gonna give you some local,' he said. 'It'll ease the pain. Not that I doubt you can handle pain after what you've just been through.'

He finished stitching her up, all the while asking if she was okay. She'd kept her eyes fixed on her baby in the crib the entire time. But she still couldn't see clearly through the thick glass. She was desperate for a *proper* glimpse, or better, to actually hold her little one.

'There we go,' the Aussie doctor finally said. 'You've done very well, Miss Reilly. The hard part's over now. I'll be back to check on the two of you tomorrow.'

The midwife, whose forehead still shone with beads of sweat, clenched Bridget's hand and gave her a smile.

'Well done, Miss Reilly,' she said. 'You've got to be the quietest first-timer I've ever seen. But, unlucky for me, you won't be the *last* woman I'll see tonight. Must be the bloody full moon or something ... everyone seems to be popping. Take care, dear.'

'Thank you,' Bridget said as the midwife hurriedly left the room with the two doctors.

One of the young nurses then bathed her with a warm cloth while the other nurse cleared away the blood that had pooled at the bottom of the bed. The two nurses chatted to each other like most young Irish women do – at a rate of a million words a minute. They giggled and laughed and gossiped as they worked away, cleaning Bridget up. But she was paying no attention to them. Her eyes couldn't be drawn away from her baby in the glass crib. The little girl was wrapped in a white blanket, her face turned out of sight. She was just a little bundle, Bridget's very own little bundle. She wanted to reach out and touch her, but the crib was too far away. So she just continued to stare, perfectly content, happy beyond words, intrinsically in love at first sight, even if it was through the distorted blur of a glass crib.

'Miss Reilly, we need to take ye down to the room now,' one of the nurses said. 'Do ye want to hold her on the way down?'

Bridget's lips spread into an overwhelming grin. 'I'd love to,' she replied.

One of the young nurses lifted the little girl from the glass crib and carried her to Bridget's side, slowly lowering the precious white bundle into her waiting arms. That's when she properly saw her tiny face for the first time, poking out from the blanket. She was instantly in awe of every part of her. Her little nose, her tiny hands and feet, her pursed lips, her pink-blotched cheeks and jet-black hair. And what a head of hair it was. A dense, dark mop of fur covered her scalp. It definitely wasn't an inheritance of the Reilly genes. She could feel the gentle tapping of her little girl's heart beating against her chest. She was so small, so fragile, yet her existence so astoundingly powerful. Bridget was transfixed by her. All the fear, the denial, and the shame seemed to instantly wash away, just like the excruciating pain had earlier. Simply holding her little girl in her arms ignited a new strength within Bridget – a sort of invincibility, a belief that she could conquer *anything* for the good of the child in her arms.

Off they went, rattling out the door on the creaky old hospital bed. The young Irish nurses tried to steer the bed around a corner, but the rickety wheels wouldn't budge. The bed was swerving all over the corridor like an out-of-control bumper car. The two young nurses couldn't control themselves either as they giggled hysterically.

'Jesus, Donna. Left. Left!' one of the nurses yelled.

'I'm pushin' left, Maggie! The feckin' ting won't move,' the other nurse replied.

'My arse, it won't move. Push harder! We're terribly sorry, Miss Reilly.'

'Jaysus! You're gonna hit the wall. Pull back!'

'Terribly sorry, Miss Reilly. We should have just *carried* ye to the room.'

'Push left.'

'I'm feckin' pushin' left. You push right!'

'The stupid ting won't budge! Jaysus Christ. Terribly sorry, Miss Reilly. Hold on! Don't drop the wee one.'

The nurses got into a fit of giggles. And it was contagious. Bridget laughed with them. She hadn't laughed in such a long time. She couldn't remember the last time she'd laughed like this. But having just safely brought her little girl into the world, she felt as though she was perhaps *allowed* to laugh again.

They eventually made it to the hospital room in one piece, not that Bridget was ever worried they wouldn't. No matter how erratic the bumpy ride became, there was no way she'd let her baby out of her grasp. Her eyes were still glued to her. She couldn't look away. She felt a bond being born between them. Even though she'd only been holding her little girl for a few minutes, she'd been a part of Bridget for nine months. And as she kissed her for the first time on her crinkled forehead, she realised that she'd *always* be a part of her. It was a bond that could never be broken.

I love you … Reynagh. That was one of the many names she'd considered during the final months of her pregnancy. But it was only now that she was looking down at her cute little face, thick black hair, and big brown eyes that the name suddenly seemed to fit perfectly. It was an Irish name for a black-haired beauty whose blood would always be green, no matter where her life took her.

'Sorry 'bout the turbulence on the way up,' one of the young nurses said, smirking. 'Ye've had quite the night, haven't ya? We need to take the wee bub down to the nursery now, if ye want to say goodbye.'

Bridget didn't want to let Reynagh go. But the idea of sleep suddenly appealed to her. She was exhausted – every muscle ached, stabbed, and stung. And she was sure her little girl needed some rest as well. She kissed Reynagh again on the forehead and then handed her back to the nurses, who took her away to the nursery. As the doors closed behind them, an overpowering weight pulled at Bridget's eyelids. She was asleep within a few minutes. For the first time in nine months, she drifted off without imagining some alternative reality. She didn't need to. Everything was perfect.

Bridget woke after what felt like the longest sleep of her life. The birth had played out over and over again in her dreams. And Reynagh was, of course, her waking thought. She wanted to get up and see her straight away. She swung her legs over the side of the bed. She was still sore from head to toe, but she felt as though she had enough power in her legs to walk to the nursery. But just as she was about to get on her feet and walk out the door, it abruptly swung open. A nurse was standing in the doorway.

'And where do you think you're off to?' she asked, her eyebrows raised.

'I ... ahh,' Bridget muttered sheepishly, like a child that's been caught in the act of misbehaviour.

The nurse smirked. 'Put those legs back in bed, Miss Reilly. I know you want to see your baby. But there's no need to walk. We'll bring her to you.'

Reynagh was gently stirring in her crib when they wheeled her into the room. She was just as perfect as Bridget's memory had painted her. Bridget spent hours with her, cuddling, kissing, even just watching her sleep. She felt infatuated, fulfilled by a love that redefined her notion of love. They were eventually interrupted by the Aussie doctor. He stood in the doorway for a moment, smiling at the sight of Mum and bub.

'How are ya feeling today?' he asked.

'Grand, doctor,' Bridget replied.

'She's a beauty,' he said in his ocker Aussie accent.

'Oh yes, she's gorgeous. Thank you so much, doctor.'

'You don't need to thank me,' he said. 'You pushed her out, not me. Now, let's have a look at her. Make sure everything is working as it should be.'

The doctor spent a few minutes examining Reynagh. But he occasionally looked back at Bridget and noticed her adoring gaze.

'I've seen that look before,' he said. 'It doesn't matter how many times you see it. A new mum gawking at her little one ... it still gives you a buzz. Makes it all worth it.'

He spent a few more minutes checking the little girl, before addressing Bridget again.

'She's all good, Miss Reilly. But there is one thing I wanna chat to you about. Not that it's really my place to say anything. But I feel like I should.'

'Of course,' Bridget replied.

The Aussie doctor glanced down at Reynagh, then back at Bridget. He opened his mouth to speak, then snapped it shut, apparently hesitant to say the words aloud.

'Are you ... going to *keep* her?' he finally asked.

Bridget was lost for words.

CHAPTER NINE

THE HUSBANDS

'Are you going to keep her?'

'I ... ah ... oh ...' Bridget mumbled. 'Of course I *want* to keep her, doctor ...'

'But ...' he interjected. 'Do you have someone you can talk to? Are your parents supporting you?'

She considered lying. *Of course they are. They were just held up in Bradford so they couldn't be here for the birth. But they're rushing to my bedside as we speak. They can't wait to meet their beautiful little granddaughter!*

'No,' she finally admitted.

The Aussie doctor sat down on the end of Bridget's bed, chin in hand as he appeared to be very carefully considering his next words.

'Hmm. Look, I'm only saying this because I see the way you look at her. Believe it or not, some of the other women in your shoes don't look at their babies the same way. It's like they don't want to get too attached ... because it'll just make it harder when they have to say goodbye. I don't blame 'em, really.'

The doctor grabbed Bridget's hand and gave it a gentle squeeze. 'But as for you, Miss Reilly, it's pretty plain to see that you're already smitten. And at least you've something on your side. Time. There's still plenty of it. She's barely been around for a day. So this whole thing probably hasn't even hit you yet. I am sorry to have to put the question in your head at this moment. But it's something you need to think about, sooner rather than later. Because you've still got time. But ... once you haven't got time on your side any more ... there's no going back.'

The doctor looked away from Bridget and got to his feet. 'But I know where you've come here from,' he continued. 'And I know your options are ... limited.'

He glanced down at Reynagh, then back at Bridget, curling his lips into a smile. 'She really is a beauty,' he said, before leaving the room.

Bridget stared down at Reynagh's tiny sleeping face, savouring the sight of it. And she wondered how many more times she'd get to see it.

Later that afternoon, a nurse came to collect Reynagh and return her to the nursery. Bridget's blood results had improved since the birth, so she was told she'd be moved to a shared room the following morning, where she'd be alongside other women who had also just given birth.

Unlike the journey from the delivery room several days earlier, the wheels of the hospital bed barely rattled as she was taken to her new room. This journey was also free of young Irish nurses cursing and giggling at the top of their lungs as they tried to steer that bed. Bridget arrived to find three women in white hospital gowns sitting up in their beds and chatting among themselves. All three of the women looked a little rundown, with their hair frayed and eyes red, with blackish-blue bags clouded under them. But they all had a certain glow about them, a certain looseness in their faces amid toothy grins.

'Hiya,' they muttered in unison as Bridget was wheeled into the room and set up along the wall next to them. Patricia was the first woman to introduce herself. She was just a few years older than Bridget, in her mid-twenties. Patricia had dark skin, similar to the colour of Amir's, but she spoke with the accent of a true Epping local. She didn't seem embarrassed to admit she had 'screamed the house down' during her labour.

'It was bloody horrible,' she said. 'Lasted two bloody days. They told me it was gonna be hard because it was my first. But I wasn't expecting it to be like that. Especially when they got the bloody forceps out. Hopefully the next one just falls out now.'

Wendy was the oldest woman in the room. She had short black curly hair and panda-like black bags under her eyes – the apparent remnants of days without sleep.

'Just had my fourth,' Wendy said. 'And get this ... they're all girls! The husband can't believe it. Poor sod. All he ever wanted was a little lad so he could play football for England. Not that my husband was ever any good at sport. The fat bastard couldn't run a mile to save himself.' She laughed heartily. 'But I don't mind having another girl,' she continued. 'Makes it easier to gang up on George ... my husband, that is. He's definitely got his hands full at the moment, looking after our other children while I'm in here with bub. But this is a holiday for me. There are three screaming children and a screaming husband at home. I much prefer the sleeping one that's in the nursery downstairs. Plus, in here we've got breakfast, lunch, and dinner delivered in bed. This place is bloody paradise!'

Sandy was the final woman to introduce herself to Bridget. She had short blonde hair, large spectacles magnifying the size of her green eyes, and wore a gold cross around her neck. She was also wearing an unbroken smile, creating a little indent on either cheek.

'My husband and I almost gave up,' Sandy told Bridget. 'I fell pregnant three times. But the Lord took them all away from us before we had the chance to meet them. Now they're little angels in heaven, where they'll always look down on us. But ... I selfishly didn't want more angels. I wanted a baby that I could hold and hug and watch grow. I prayed every night, for years, asking for a miracle. And then, yesterday, it finally happened. Our little girl, Majella, came into the world at 2:57 p.m. We named her Majella after Saint Majella. You know her, Bridget? She's the patron saint of pregnant women.'

It didn't take Bridget long to notice something that her three roommates had in common, apart from having just given birth. Patricia, Wendy, and Sandy were all wearing wedding rings. The gold bands gleamed under the fluorescent lights and against their white hospital gowns. Bridget suddenly felt very aware of her left hand, so she buried it within her gown, out of sight. All three of the women were from the Epping area, so Bridget suspected they knew she'd come from the local mother and baby home. But as they chatted and laughed over breakfast, sharing their experiences from the delivery room, none of the women asked her anything about the father of her child.

Later in the morning, the doors of the room swung open. A nurse walked through, wheeling a crib with a small child within it. Sandy let out a little whimper at the sight of the baby. Her eyes were glassy, her arms outstretched as the nurse lifted the child out of the crib and into her waiting arms. Another nurse then walked through the door, pushing another crib with another infant. The little baby was tossing and turning in the crib, screaming and bawling its eyes out.

'Shhh,' Wendy said, taking hold of the child. 'Big cry-baby! Just like your sisters ... and your daddy. Come to Mumma.'

A third nurse walked through the door, wheeling a crib with a dark-skinned boy in it. Joy overtook Patricia's face at the sight of him, before he was handed over to her. Bridget's eyes were glued to the doorway, waiting for Reynagh to appear. For a moment, a breathless moment, it seemed like she wouldn't. Perhaps the Reverend Mother had made arrangements to take Reynagh away during the night, Bridget feared. But then, relief came upon her, as a nurse entered, wheeling Reynagh in a crib. The little girl's arms and legs were outstretched, her big brown eyes staring around curiously at the new surroundings. The nurse lifted her into Bridget's arms.

'Isn't she gorgeous?' Wendy said, staring over at Reynagh.

'She is,' Bridget responded, the proud mother within her finding voice.

'That hair!' Patricia chimed in. 'There's so much of it. It's beautiful.'

'She's a blessing,' Sandy added, also smiling towards Reynagh.

'Thank you,' Bridget said. 'All your babies look lovely as well. Just as cute as you described them.'

'Yeah, they *look* lovely,' Wendy, the oldest mother, said. 'But just wait till they start shitting every five minutes ... and that's in between all the throwing up and screaming. They don't look so *lovely* then.'

The four of them laughed, then turned their attention back to their little ones. Bridget couldn't imagine ever thinking Reynagh was anything other than lovely.

The day passed, with the four mothers cuddling their newborns and chatting. Patricia, Wendy, and Sandy had so many compliments for Reynagh. 'Those little feet, how cute ... Listen to her cough, what an angel ... Those brown eyes could pierce through steel ... She's beautiful ... gorgeous ... lovely ... an absolute joy ... a miracle ... a blessing ...'

The women made such a big deal of Reynagh. Bridget thought it might have been because they thought she was different to the other children. But whatever the reason, their kindness was enough to bring Bridget to the verge of tears.

At 5 p.m., it was visiting time. And there were strict rules about who was allowed to visit. It was reserved for the most important person in the baby's life, other than the mother. From 5 p.m. till 7 p.m. every night, it was all about the husbands. Within seconds of the clock ticking past five, the doors of the room swung open again. Three men filed in, each of them holding flowers and gifts.

'About time!' Wendy, the oldest mother, yelled out jovially at the sight of her husband. Her husband, George, a man in his mid-thirties, looked dishevelled with an unshaven face and ragged red hair. He looked more ragged than his wife, despite the fact she'd only given birth a day earlier. He placed a bouquet of flowers on Wendy's bedside table as she lifted the child into his arms.

'She's smaller than I remember,' George said.

'Easy for you to say!' Wendy snapped back. 'You didn't have to push her out.'

George chuckled as he gawked down at the child in his arms. 'S'pose another girl isn't so bad after all,' he said.

Patricia, the mother who'd endured a horrible labour, was

next to be greeted by her husband, Anthony. Anthony was carrying a bunch of white flowers and a little blue teddy bear. Their boy started to cry as he approached.

'He knows his daddy's here,' Patricia said as Anthony picked up the baby and cradled him, kissing his crinkled forehead.

James, Sandy's husband, was the last man through the door. He was holding red roses in one hand and a bible in the other. He stopped at the end of Sandy's bed, tears welling in his eyes, his jaw hanging open as he stared at their little girl who was rocking in Sandy's arms. He placed the flowers and the bible on the bedside table and reached out towards his little girl, delicately brushing his fingers against her soft rosy cheeks. Tears were streaming down Sandy's face as she watched her husband bond with their child. Bridget smiled. After all the pain this young couple had endured, they *finally* had their little miracle.

'You can pick her up, you know,' Sandy said to James.

James appeared to hesitate for a moment, as though he wasn't yet qualified to hold the baby. He very slowly and carefully lifted the child and held her to his chest, gently rocking her back and forth.

'She's so...'

'Perfect,' Sandy cut in.

'I was going to say small,' James said. 'But yeah. She's just ... perfect.'

Sandy and James smiled at each other, wiping away their tears as they gazed at the baby between them.

Bridget acknowledged the three husbands with a smile. She then grabbed a book from her side table and buried her head in it. The words blurred before her eyes, appearing as nothing more than black squiggled lines on the page. She didn't look away. She couldn't bring herself to watch the loving reunions happening around her. But while she could shield her eyes, she couldn't escape the laughing, the gasps, the sniffling of joyous weeping, and the 'oohs' and 'ahhs'. The room was buzzing with fatherly love. She tried not to dwell on it, but being surrounded by adoring husbands was just another reminder that she did not have one. And it was a reminder that Reynagh did not have a father at her side.

Reynagh might not have known any better at that moment, but Bridget feared she would one day reach an age when she *would* know better. She'd realise her dad was not around. She'd be the child without a father in her life, just as she was in the hospital room. As though sensing her fatherless future, Reynagh started to cry. She hadn't cried like this before. It was a shrill and bone-chilling shriek. Bridget threw her book aside and grabbed her from the crib, wrapping her in a warm embrace.

'Shh, beautiful girl,' Bridget said. 'It's okay. Your mammy's here.'

She rocked her back and forth, and Reynagh's cries gradually softened. As she did this, she noticed some sideways glances from the visiting husbands.

'Shh,' Bridget muttered again. 'You're alright, darling. Hush now.'

Wendy pulled her husband in close and whispered something in his ear. Bridget could feel their eyes staring in her direction.

'Bridget!' Wendy yelled out. 'This is my husband, George. George, this is Bridget. Our Irish friend.'

George held his hand out to greet her, which she shook. 'Looks like you've got your hands full there,' he said, pointing at Reynagh.

Bridget nodded, smiling.

'She's a cute one though,' George continued. 'Because trust me, after having four girls, I know they ain't always pretty when they come out. Our first couple came out with squashed heads ... shaped like bloody turnips they were.'

He giggled.

'Careful there, George!' Wendy barked at her husband. 'You're in a room full of women. We'll make your head look like a squashed turnip if you don't watch your mouth.'

Patricia also turned towards Bridget and called out. 'Bridget,' she said. 'This is my husband, Anthony.'

'And this is James,' Sandy chimed in.

James and Anthony left their wives and newborns and came over to Bridget's bedside. They also held their hands out to greet her.

'God bless you, Bridget,' James said. 'It really is a miracle, isn't it?'

'Yes, it is,' Bridget replied.

'She's very pretty,' Anthony said, referring to Reynagh.

'Oh yes,' James added. 'Very pretty.'

'So very pretty,' George chimed in. 'Definitely no turnip-head here! She's a little looker alright!'

'Thank you all very much,' Bridget said. 'If she was old enough to understand your words, she'd feel very special indeed.'

The husbands spent a few more minutes making a fuss out of Reynagh, just like their wives had earlier in the day. It brought a smile to Bridget's face. After all, the other mothers and their husbands had no obligation to make her feel better. But still, they tried to include Reynagh and her in the 'happy family' celebrations. A happy family – how nice that would have been, she thought. She wondered if her mammy and daddy were thinking about her and the baby. *Are they wondering if the birth went smoothly? Do they want to know what their grandchild looks like? Do they want to hold her ... feel her touch ... hug and kiss her? Do they even* care *how we're doing?*

There were, of course, no answers to those questions to be found in the hospital room. All Bridget could do was guess what was going through her parents' minds. Perhaps her mammy and daddy were just praying the situation would go away. At least then they wouldn't have to carry out their plan and hide the baby with Aunty Ellen. Perhaps they'd just resigned themselves to the fact that Bridget was now an unmarried mother, and as such would not be part of the Reilly family any more. Perhaps they lived in fear that Bridget and her newborn would be condemned to the depths of hell for eternity (as some back in Ireland strongly believed was the case for anyone who was a party to unwed conception). Perhaps, perhaps, perhaps ... The truth was, she had no idea what her parents were actually thinking. But she suspected, without question, that they were ashamed. So ashamed, in fact, they couldn't swallow their pride and come to Epping to see their granddaughter and share in the miracle of her birth.

They stayed in the hospital for three more nights. Bridget spent the days enjoying the company of Wendy, Patricia, and Sandy as they bonded with their newborns. But every afternoon at 5 p.m., their husbands came to visit. Without fail, Reynagh cried every time. Bridget focused on cradling her back to calmness, rocking her back and forth while trying to ignore the precious family moments happening around them.

Her stay at the hospital ended when a nun from the mother and baby home arrived just after breakfast.

'*Miss* Reilly,' the nun said, emphasising the 'Miss' as though making a point. 'It's time to leave.'

Bridget hugged the other mothers and said goodbye, knowing she'd probably never see them again. Wendy, the oldest mother in the room, called out to her just before she exited through the door.

'Don't forget about our spare pram!' Wendy said. 'It's all yours. I don't want you being overly polite. You have to take it. And it's a good one as well. She won't fall out of it!'

'That's very kind of you,' Bridget replied.

'It's so beautiful outside at the moment,' Wendy said. 'We can go for a walk together with the little ones.'

Bridget smiled, picturing Reynagh resting peacefully in a pram as she walked with her in the summer sun alongside Wendy and her child. It was a nice thought, at least.

The nun escorted Bridget, with Reynagh in her arms, to a taxi waiting in the front driveway of the hospital. She glanced back at the building one last time as they rolled away. She'd truly felt lucky within that hospital. Yes, she'd given birth surrounded by strangers and without her parents around. But at least it was *in* a hospital. She'd heard stories about other unmarried mothers who were not as lucky. There were stories of women giving birth in bathrooms, cars, even on the street. Those women were truly alone for what should have been one of the most precious moments of their lives. But Bridget felt so thankful for the way the doctors, nurses, and midwives treated her at Epping Hospital. She was treated like a human being, a mother giving birth to a baby. She wasn't treated like an *unmarried* mother, even though the staff at Epping Hospital had no doubt seen countless cases like hers over the years, churned out from the mother and baby home.

She stared out the window at the green fields as the taxi made its way along the winding roads back to the mother and baby home. She couldn't stop thinking about her roommates from the hospital: Wendy, Patricia, and Sandy. Their homeward journey would be so different to this. They'd go home with their babies and begin their long and happy lives together. They had so much to look forward to: hearing their child speak for the first time, watching them take their first stumbling step, and then there would be all their birthday parties, their first day of school, and school dances, and Christmas mornings, and family holidays, and everything in between. Wendy, Patricia, and Sandy would leave the hospital knowing their future with their children would last as long as they did. But Bridget and Reynagh's future was *not* clear. Their path together was only visible for six weeks. Beyond that, there was no path – just the uncharted wilderness.

Six weeks. That's how long Bridget and Reynagh would be allowed to stay at the mother and baby home before being ushered back into the real world. As the taxi edged closer to the home, over the same roads on which she had battled contractions just days earlier, Bridget vowed to cherish every moment of the next six weeks. The clock was ticking. And unlike the staff, mothers, and their husbands she had encountered at Epping Hospital, *time* would show no mercy.

PRESENT

CHAPTER TEN

THE NEWSROOM

The emergency services radio scanner blasts in my right ear. 'Arrived at house fire,' a muffled voice comes through the speaker. 'We've checked the alarm – set off by burnt toast. No backup needed. We've made up, and we're returning to the station.'

While I keep my right ear on that, my left ear is tuned in to talkback radio. There's a heated debate between the government and opposition about state debt and who's to blame for it. Three screens sit on the desk in front of me. On the left screen, there's a live scroll of Twitter and Facebook, which is usually the first place news appears these days. On my centre screen, there's a steady flow of emails – from police press releases about major crimes, to local companies trying to pitch stories that are really blatant ads for their products, to emails from unhappy viewers who are complaining about the way a word was pronounced in last night's bulletin. On my right screen, I flick between our two commercial

TV news rivals so we be aware of any stories they've got that we don't.

The newsroom around me is buzzing as deadline looms. Producers yell from their desks for editors to post stories or they'll miss their spots in the bulletin. Journos yell back, 'Not far away!' On the other side of the newsroom, techies are busy checking the lights, cameras, and microphones in the studio before we go on air. The room is full of the sounds of frantically typing keyboards, people yelling critical instructions, ringing phones, and a muffle of shuffling papers and footsteps as staff move around the building with the same urgency you'd expect in a NASA control room.

And here I am, in the middle of it all. I'm no longer a storyteller, out in the trenches gathering information and reporting it to the masses. Instead, I'm the one back at base, liaising with the foot soldiers and plotting our next move on the battlefield that is daily news. As chief of staff in the newsroom, I have to be on top of everything that's happening throughout Perth. That means everything we're covering for the nightly news, and everything we're *not* covering, which I'll probably be blamed for missing.

I'm the first person to get into the office every day when it's dark and quiet and all the desks are empty. From then on, it's non-stop as I try to compile the news of the day and start assigning journalists and camera operators to cover it. It's not a physically demanding job. I mean, I sit on my arse all day long. But it's definitely mentally draining. The constant scanning of information on multiple screens while listening to information from multiple speakers certainly puts my cognitive ability to the test. And by the time I leave the office at the end of each day, my brain is usually a fried mess. But lately, my job in the newsroom has been somewhat of an escape.

I've been so invested in Mum's story, I've become consumed by it. I spend every day off working on it, whether through writing or research. And when I'm not working on it, I'm thinking about it. So working in the newsroom has actually been a nice distraction. Daily television news with its car crashes and house fires, dickhead criminals, police pursuits, bickering politicians, and animals stuck up trees, although at times trivial, at least doesn't hit as close to home as Mum's story does.

'Dan!' one of the producers yells at me. 'Have you seen there's a police pursuit in South Perth? The other stations are crossing live from there! Why don't we know about this?'

Shit! I scan through the police computer system to find it. There it is. 'Police pursuit, South Perth' – the note is right there in front of me. Damn, I missed this one.

'On it!' I yell back at the producers as I scan the newsroom with my eyes to find a journalist and camera operator to send. Once that's attended to, I sink into my chair and hide behind my screens, hoping to avoid eye contact with my fuming producers. I turn my focus to Twitter to see if there's any update from journos at the pursuit scene. But it's a tweet about something else that steals my focus. My eyes, dreary from the pre-dawn start, widen as I read the headline in front of me.

'Dead Babies Found in Sewer of Ex-Home for Unwed Mothers.'

I read the headline again a few times, but I'm unable to comprehend the words. I start searching through my newsfeeds, where more headlines stand out as though they're the only words on the screen.

'Mass Graves Found at Former Irish Orphanage.'

'Up to 800 Children Found Underground at a Former Home for Unmarried Mothers and their Babies in Ireland.'

'Remains of Young Children and Babies Found in Sewage Chambers at Tuam Mother and Baby Home.'

I check out the website for the Mother and Baby Homes Commission of Investigation – the entity appointed by the Irish Government to investigate treatment at these institutions in their country in the past century. A few clicks and I've substantiated the claims in the headlines. The Commission confirms it in writing:

'Significant quantities of human remains uncovered ... their ages ranging from 35 foetal weeks to 2–3 years ... the chamber in which they were found appears to be related to the treatment/containment of sewage and/or waste water.'

It's true. I gasp. The Commission of Investigation doesn't confirm the exact number that's mentioned in the headlines. But they don't dispute it either, describing it as 'significant quantities'. It's hard enough to imagine *one* child being treated like this in death. But hundreds ... up to eight hundred ... that's inconceivable. I scan through the headlines again, and all I can see is that number – eight hundred.

I suppose it's like when you see a news report about a bomb blast somewhere overseas, in which hundreds are killed. You hear it and think *that's horrible*. But you don't quite grasp the bloody reality of it. You don't see the faces of each of the men, women, and children as they took their final breaths before the blast went off – and then see what was left of them afterwards. You don't hear the wailing mother, trying to find her child among the debris and body parts. You don't see the blood staining the rubble of flattened buildings. You don't smell the overpowering stench of smoke, and dust, and death. You simply hear the news 'hundreds killed in bomb blast', and you react in the appropriate way. *That's terrible,* you think. And then you forget about it and get on with your day.

'Up to eight hundred babies.' I read it again and again. It's just a number. Yes, it's written in headlines with the most horrific connotations attached to it. But it's still just a number. It doesn't carry any justice for the individuals it represents. Each of those dead babies was once a human being, with a beating heart and developing mind. Whether death came upon them in the womb, or during birth, or after several years of living at the mother and baby home, they were still human. Now they've been reduced to a number in a horror story.

'Dan, any word from the crew about the pursuit in South Perth?' one of the producers yells again.

'Ah, not yet,' I say.

Police pursuit – who bloody cares about that? It's not *real* news. Everything happening around me suddenly feels so much less important. All I can think about are those headlines. I go through each of the articles, scouring over every line for as much detail as possible. My heart thuds heavily in my chest. I close my eyes for a moment and something strange happens that makes me grasp the reality of it. I see a small child, a newborn. Her eyes are closed, her lips blue. She's wrapped in a white sheet on a metal table in an otherwise empty room. She's so still, so cold and stiff, so alone, so lifeless. I snap my eyes open. I can't do this. It's too real. I can't handle seeing their faces, even if it's only my mind playing tricks on me. I close the articles and try to focus on something else, anything else.

One of the camera operators yells out 'One minute!' Deadline is almost upon us. The news will be on air soon. I start filtering through emails that I have missed while reading the articles about the mother and baby home. I try to focus on work, but I can't. All I can think about are those children. Those poor children who should have had their lives ahead of them. But for whatever reason, whether it was unavoidable ill health, or neglect, or pure misfortune, their lives ended far sooner than they should have. That tragedy alone should have been enough to conquer the pride that kept their existence hidden. They should have been given a proper send-off with mourners, with the prayers and well wishes of the local townspeople, with flowers and hymns, and of course a little coffin in which their remains could return to the earth with some dignity. But no, dignity for the children must not have been on the minds of those who decided to dump them in mass graves in the sunless depths of underground chambers among remnants of shit and piss and puke. No crosses sat upon their graves. There was no place their mothers could go and mourn. Their existence was simply wiped from the face of the earth. Until now.

'Three, two, one ... cue.' The news opener rolls and we're on air. Talking ceases across the newsroom as the orchestral intro music plays, followed by the velvety voice of the newsreader. 'Good evening, first tonight ...'

I can't sit still in my chair. I have no interest in watching the bulletin that we've spent the day putting together. I'm clenching my teeth together, cracking my knuckles. I take a deep breath and try to calm down. But I can't. I'm so furious, so heartbroken that something so barbaric took place in Ireland – a country I've been so proud to have descended from. Yet it seems pride itself is to blame for one of Ireland's most despicable secrets.

I've had enough for the day. I pack up my things and log off my computer. I sneak out of the newsroom while everyone's eyes are focused on the bulletin that's playing on various screens around the office. Even after I drive home, and go for a run, and cook dinner, and watch some trashy reality TV with my girlfriend, Jen, all I can think about are those headlines. And as I close my eyes and try to drift off to sleep later that night, all I can see is that one nameless child I pictured in my mind earlier. And all I can think is that this one poor child has not been remembered by name. She's been reduced to a number.

I've been researching mother and baby homes for months. I'm somewhat ashamed to say I didn't know they even existed until Mum started sharing her story with me. How naïve does that make me? How sheltered? How fortunate, I guess? Fortunate that such a thing doesn't exist in my country, in my lifetime. I want to learn as much as I can about this shameful era while telling Mum's story. Others my age need to know about this. It can't simply be forgotten.

I've spent countless hours in my days off delving into the world of mother and baby homes. I've discovered advocate groups for unmarried mothers, government departments, historical books, memoirs, reports, journals, documentaries, even big budget films. All of it opens my eyes to a world that neither I nor most people my age can relate to. Through my research, I learn that Mum's account of the Catholic mother and baby home she attended in Epping is but a tiny glimpse of what was a far-reaching practice. These homes were run by Church and state. And while each home was run slightly differently, they all seem to have shared the same culture of silence and, of course, shame.

Meanwhile, I'm learning more about Mum's experience as a young unmarried mother, during each conversation. Several nights a week, we spend hours on the phone as I poke and prod her for details. And that's what's happening this particular Sunday night – the first since I read those awful stories about the dead babies. We're chatting about her time in Epping Hospital after giving birth to Reynagh. It heartens me to hear the warmth in her words when she talks about holding her little girl for the first time. But I hate hearing her voice quiver when she talks about being alone and not having anyone there with her and Reynagh while the husbands of the other mothers came to visit. I always want to stop when she gets upset. But she always insists that we keep going. So we do. She describes everything about her days in the hospital after the birth in as much detail as she can remember. We chat for hours before she gets to the part when she's about to return to the mother and baby home with Reynagh for the first time.

'We were allowed to stay at the home for six weeks,' she says over the phone. 'Six weeks. Have I mentioned that, Danny?'

'Yes, you have, Mum,' I say.

'Well,' she continues, 'the nuns took us back there. Reynagh and I ... and then ... hold on. Oh I'm sorry, there's a call coming through. Is it alright if we chat about it another time?'

'No worries,' I say, despite desperately wanting to know what happens next. 'We've probably gone through enough for tonight anyway. I'll ring you tomorrow.'

We hang up. I stare at my computer screen in the spare room of our apartment. I've assembled a compilation of historical images as part of my research. I'm looking at a black-and-white photo of a nursery, filled with about a dozen white, steel cribs, a baby in each of them. Four nuns, covered head to toe in white gowns with just their faces popping out from their headpieces, are standing next to the cribs. I click on the next photo. It's quite similar to the last, although the infants are slightly older in this one. They're probably about eighteen months old, and they're standing within their white, steel cots, their tiny hands gripping around the metal frames as they stare blankly at the camera. Once again, the nuns are standing over them. It's quite depressing. A snapshot of misery, you could call it.

I keep scrolling through the archives. I want to paint a picture for myself, an understanding of what those places were really like. Each photo is about as miserable as the last, with hardly a smile to be seen. Eventually, I come across a photo in which a young woman is walking into a mother and baby home. Her belly is delicately bulging beneath a heavy duffel coat. She's looking away from the camera, but her shoulders are hunched forward, her head bowed downward. It could be my mother in this photo for all I know. I slam my laptop shut. I've had enough for today. And I fear what I'll learn during my next phone call with Mum. What did she and Reynagh endure during their six weeks? It worries me even more now that the stories about dead babies being dumped in that Irish home have come out.

I go to bed, trying to turn my mind to other less concerning things. But when I fall asleep, my dreams take me there – to 1971, when Mum returned to the mother and baby home after giving birth to Reynagh.

Like most dreams, the start is a bit of a blur. I don't know where I am, or what's happening. Then, things become clearer. I spot my mother. She's younger than me, just twenty-one years old. She's on the concrete floor, on her hands and knees, scrubbing with a steel brush as sweat builds on her forehead. I move towards her and hold out my hand.

'Mum, take my hand.'

She can't hear me. She keeps scrubbing, as though I'm not even there. The screeching sound makes me want to block my ears. But I also want to pick her up and help her to a chair where she can rest her legs. Her knees must be red raw on that uneven concrete floor. Even though she doesn't look like she's carrying a baby within her any more, she still looks like she's carrying something – a burden, perhaps. I can see it in the way her shoulders are hunched forward, her head bowed, just like the woman in the photo I saw earlier.

'Mum!'

I'm yelling as loud as I can. But she still can't hear me.

I notice a nun in the corner of the room watching over Mum. It's the Reverend Mother. Her sour, wrinkled face stares expressionlessly at Mum as she performs the back-breaking labour. I walk over to the Reverend Mother, towering over her. I stare straight into her beady black eyes – they're void of any warmth, just like the cold concrete floor.

'You're a fuckin' disgrace!' I say. 'What sort of a Catholic are you meant to be?'

The Reverend Mother stares straight through me, at my poor helpless mother as she scrubs the filthy floor.

Suddenly, I'm in a different place. It's dark and cold. And I'm surrounded by babies that are scattered across the damp concrete floor. None of them are moving. Not again, I tell myself. It's just a dream! I'm suddenly overcome with a crippling despair. Then, anger fires within me. I scream with rage. *How could this happen!* But no sound comes out. No one's listening. No one cares.

BEEP. BEEP. BEEP.

My alarm goes off. It's 4:30 a.m. I've been having dreams like this for days. But right now, I don't have time to lie here and think about it or attempt to analyse it. I have to get ready for another day in the newsroom. I make my way into the office, my mind a mess from the dream, from the latest conversation with Mum, from the stories about the human remains at the mother and baby home in Ireland, from all I've learnt in my research. It's not only heartbreaking to watch my mother's story unfold before my eyes – it's infuriating too. As I learn more about her experience and piece the dots together through my own inquiries, I'm feeling more and more like I'm right there in the moment with her as she relives her painful past. I'm watching from the corner of a room. I'm a fly on the wall. But I'm helpless. I'm just a spectator to her pain and misery. And there's nothing I can do, except watch.

PAST

CHAPTER ELEVEN

SIX WEEKS TO GO

B EEP. BEEP. BEEP. Bridget's day started at 5 a.m. with a blaring alarm. She rolled out of bed and quickly got dressed. Time was now a precious commodity, especially in the morning. A slither of sun was peeking over the horizon as she stepped outside into the morning cold. Even though it was summer in England, there were still shards of frost covering the grass. She marched along the crumbling footpath towards the nursery, almost breaking into an enthusiastic skip. Other women filed out behind her. They, too, broke into a brisk walk as they approached the nursery.

The doors of the nursery opened, giving way to Bridget and a dozen women. They rushed in like schoolchildren at the morning opening of a sweet shop. A chorus of screaming babies filled the room, mixed with the rancid smell of soiled nappies. Bridget rushed to Reynagh's crib. Her little girl was red-faced, crying, and flailing her arms and legs about.

'Shh,' Bridget said, picking her up. 'Mammy's here now.'

All the babies seemed restless, as though they hadn't slept a wink all night. Bridget hadn't slept well either. She'd spent the night worrying about Reynagh being all alone. There was an old nun, Sister Francis, who slept in the nursery so she could look after the babies after dark. But Bridget feared that Sister Francis, who was well north of seventy, might not be able to hear the soft cries of a baby in need of care. It was pointless to worry, though. There was nothing Bridget could do. The Reverend Mother made sure the mothers and babies were kept apart after midnight.

Bridget placed Reynagh back in the crib and mixed milk powder and water in a bottle, shaking it until it formed a creamy white colour that almost resembled the real thing. There were small wooden stools beside each of the cribs, allowing the women to sit down and rest their legs while they fed their little ones. Bridget's knees cracked as she crouched down onto the stool, most likely because of all the scrubbing she'd been doing lately on her hands and knees. With Reynagh nestled in her left arm and resting on her knee, Bridget held the bottle with her right hand. Reynagh's pursed pink lips wrapped around the bottle, and she closed her eyes and sucked away. The nursery was no longer filled with the sound of screaming infants. Instead, the squelching of suckling babies took over. *Slurp, slurp, slurp.* One of the unmarried mothers suddenly started to sing.

'Late night on the dance floor,
Short girls' arms a flailing,
Tall men sing the sweet roar,
Big groups moving in sync.'
A few more of the unmarried mothers joined in with her.
'Oriental, subcontinental, dancing hand in hand.
Fat and thin, old and young ... tapping toes.
Black and white, singing like lead singers in a band.

The dance floor is the place to be, everybody knows!'

The song took hold of the room as the chorus arrived. Every unmarried mother was now singing along as though they were some sort of postnatal choir, while the babies continued to suck their bottles in unison.

'*It don't matter where you've been.*

It don't matter where you're going.

The lights beneath the disco ball shine on us, all the same.

For the dance floor don't have eyes. For the dance floor don't have eyes!'

The song, which had been considered controversial because it promoted racial equality and integration, had been a hit in the UK a couple of years earlier. But as the unmarried mothers sang, their babies happily sucking away at the end of the bottles, while the sun rose outside bringing golden light into the nursery, Bridget strangely felt more of a connection to the lyrics than any hymn she'd ever sung in church. She glanced around at the other women - the nursery of singing unmarried mothers really was a great big melting pot of different races, just like the dance floor in the song. The only thing they all shared was their shame.

When the song died down and the babies were fed, the women began bathing their newborns. Reynagh's big brown eyes curiously stared up at Bridget as she lowered her into the bath until just her face lay above the surface. She didn't cry or squirm like some of the other babies. She simply stared up at her mother, appearing to enjoy the warm touch of the water on her soft skin. Bridget's was the first face she saw every morning, and the last she saw at night. If she didn't know it yet, she'd surely soon know that Bridget was her mother.

After bath time, Bridget dressed Reynagh in a frilly yellow dress that she'd bought in town the day after returning from the hospital. She brushed her silky black hair to one side and held her aloft. Bridget was grinning from ear to ear. And it was a grin that didn't fade in the thirty minutes that followed. That's how long the mothers had left until they would be summoned to the dining hall for breakfast. Thirty minutes for Bridget to touch, to hug, to simply marvel at the small bundle of life she had created. Surrounded by other young women and their babies in the midst of similar loving embraces, they were the most precious of minutes. That morning embrace gave Bridget strength to get through the rest of her day. And strength came in handy, because after breakfast at 7 a.m. it was time to get to work. Having just given birth didn't exempt Bridget and the other mothers from their daily chores. She was back in the kitchen, peeling spuds and carrots before building up a sweat scrubbing grease from the stovetop and grubby floor. But every time her wrists ached while peeling, or when her knees stung while scrubbing, she thought of Reynagh in that beautiful little yellow dress. That thought alone was enough to instantly ease any ache or pain.

By early afternoon, the food was prepared, the floors clean, the beds made, laundry done, and persistent dust through the dilapidated home wiped away for another day. That meant Bridget was free to return to the nursery and see Reynagh. And that's where she spent the rest of her day. As the hours passed within the nursery, time became Bridget's enemy. But it was an enemy she couldn't fight. It was slipping away from her, invisible and uncatchable, stealing her precious moments with Reynagh and making them possessions of the past. In Bridget's twenty-one years, she had never wanted time to stop more than she did in that nursery. But time showed no mercy. Dinner time arrived in what felt like the blink of an eye. After dinner, she returned to the nursery, where bedtime hastily approached. And then before she knew it, there was less than an hour till midnight. Reynagh was in her crib, fast asleep. As were all the other babies. It was time to say goodbye.

'Tiptoes on your way out, girls,' Sister Francis, whispered in her Dublin accent. 'And don't let the door hit your arses on the way out. Anyone that wakes a baby will feel the wrath of God himself, and the bottom of me shoe for good measure.'

Sister Francis smiled, adding more wrinkles to her already densely wrinkled face. She placed a hand on Bridget's shoulder as she was giving Reynagh a final kiss for the day.

'She'll still be here in the morning, Miss Reilly,' Sister Francis said. 'I'll be here to make sure of it. And if my eyes fail me, Saint Philomena will be looking down from above, as she does for all the wee ones who're in need of looking over.'

Back in her dorm room, Bridget lay in her bed, staring at the shadows on the ceiling. Time was still her enemy. But now instead of wanting time to slow down, she wanted it to hurry up. She longed for the morning, when she'd get to see Reynagh again, when she could feed and bath her like all *married* mothers do with their newborns. But falling asleep would mean that another day had passed. One day out of six weeks, unceremoniously gone. It felt like it had vanished into thin air, become nothing more than a memory, albeit a lovely one. The sand had well and truly started cascading through the hourglass, and there was no stopping it. Their fate was closing in on them. Bridget prayed in her bed before sleep finally came upon her.

Please, Lord. Give us more time. Six weeks is not enough.

FIVE WEEKS TO GO

One week had passed. It was a Monday morning and Bridget was in the nursery, where she had just finished feeding Reynagh with a bottle of powdered milk. The old nun, Sister Francis, approached her.

'You have a visitor, Miss Reilly,' she said.

Mammy and Daddy! Bridget thought. *They've finally come.*

Bridget arrived in the entrance hall to find a stranger, and not her parents as she had hoped, at the bottom of the forbidden staircase. It was a woman in her thirties wearing a grey jacket and skirt, with perfect shoulder-length mousy brown hair. She was holding a brown leather briefcase in one hand, a grey cloche hat in the other.

'Miss Reilly?' the woman asked.

Bridget nodded.

'I'm Linda. Can we talk in private, please?'

A nun led Bridget and Linda to an empty room where they sat down either side of a cold wooden table.

'Firstly, I need to apologise in advance,' Linda said, opening her briefcase on the table, pulling out stacks of paper, and sorting through them. 'I'm very short on time. This will just have to be a quick one today. Okay?'

'Okay,' Bridget said.

'You know why I'm here?' Linda asked.

Bridget shook her head.

'I'm your social worker,' Linda said, a little shocked that she needed to state it. 'I'm here to make things go as smoothly as possible for you and the baby.'

Linda continued sorting through the stacks of paper until she found the pages she was looking for. She clicked her pen and scribbled something at the top of the page.

'Have you thought about *what* you're looking for?' Linda asked.

Bridget looked away, taking a moment to answer. 'Yes,' she finally replied.

'Good,' Linda said. 'Well, Miss Reilly, it's as simple as you telling me what you want, and then I'll try and find the best match possible. So ... what sort of parents are we looking for?'

'No one too young,' Bridget answered.

'And why is that?'

'I don't want them going out on the town like young people do. I don't want Reynagh being left at home with strangers while her parents are out getting fluthered.'

'Fluthered?' Linda asked, looking bewildered.

'Drunk.'

'Oh, I see,' Linda said, quickly scribbling down notes on the page in front of her.

'If they have other children,' Bridget said, 'that would be good as well. 'Twould be nice for Reynagh to have brothers and sisters to play with.'

'We can *try* and accommodate that,' Linda said, scribbling away.

'And I want her baptised,' Bridget went on. 'The parents have to be Catholic.'

Linda finished writing some notes and then looked up at Bridget.

'So we're looking for a couple that is willing to adopt ... not too young ... Catholic ... and, preferably, they have *other* children?'

Bridget nodded. 'And you have to be *sure* they're going to treat her well. Even if you're just a little bit unsure about them, I don't want them getting her. They have to be good people. You need to know that, without any doubt.' She spoke with firm authority, a far cry from the shy girl with a crumbling voice who'd moved to London a few years earlier.

Linda clasped her hands together on the table and addressed Bridget like a doctor delivering a bad prognosis to a patient.

'Miss Reilly,' she said. 'You know there's only a six-week period of tenancy allowed after the birth? And there's no guarantee we'll find a family in that time. There are cases like yours in mother and baby homes in every town and village across the country. That's a lot of babies in need of a lot of families. If we can't find what you're looking for within six weeks, the baby will have to be put into care. You know … an orphanage.'

Bridget's chest seized up at the very mention of that word.

'I know it's difficult,' Linda said. 'But this is for the best.' She flicked through the papers in front of her, running her finger down the page until she found what she was looking for.

'You earn … ten pounds a month, after laundry and board, from your job as a nurse in London. You live in a modest dorm in crowded sleeping quarters at the hospital. Miss Reilly, a child needs space to grow up. You can't raise a child on ten pounds a month. And you can't do it without a husband.'

Bridget could feel the increasing weight of tears building in her eyes.

'There are some things I need to tell you before we proceed,' Linda said. 'I need you to listen very carefully and take in what I'm saying. Because there'll be no going back.'

Bridget nodded, then wiped the tears that were now trickling down her cheek.

'*If* we find suitable parents,' Linda continued, 'and *when* you hand over custody, that will be the end of it.'

Bridget took a deep, albeit shaky, breath and tried to comprehend Linda's words. *Is it really as simple as that? Does it have to be so imminent? So eternally binding?*

'I won't be able to tell you where they live,' Linda went on. 'There will be no way you can find them. And you will actually be breaking the law if you try. I need you to know that ... you will be *legally* forbidden from contacting the parents or the child.'

Bridget nodded, almost involuntarily, as Linda went on.

'And by law, the parents will have to tell the child that she is adopted. So she'll know from a young age. But it will be entirely up to her if she wants to track you down when she's of age, of course.'

'Of age?' Bridget asked.

'Eighteen,' Linda replied. 'I really need you to understand all of this, Miss Reilly. Because when the time comes to say goodbye, you'll only have *one* chance to do it.'

Linda finished writing something on the papers in front of her, then put them back in her briefcase before clipping it shut.

'I'm going to do everything I can to find the right parents for the child,' she said. 'But there's a lot of other cases I need to see to as well. Like I said, there are no guarantees for your child, unfortunately.'

Linda glanced at her watch and sprung to her feet. 'I'm sorry, I must be going. More mothers to meet with. I'll be in touch, Miss Reilly.'

FOUR WEEKS TO GO

Two weeks had passed, at a pace so quick Bridget thought the calendar must be wrong. She felt the end closing in. But she and

Reynagh were not always alone, at least, as they awaited their destiny. Mary, Teresa, and Brenda made the journey from London to visit them. Visitors were not allowed to get too close to the babies, which meant the girls could only get a glimpse of Reynagh through the nursery window. Bridget went in and carried her to the glass that bordered the corridor where the girls were waiting. Their faces lit up at the sight of Reynagh, their mouths dropping open before coiling into large grins, their eyes widening with delight. Bridget stood at the window, rocking Reynagh back and forth in her arms as the girls on the other side gushed at her cuteness. She could even hear their words through the glass. 'She's bloody gorgeous ... what a little miracle! She's got your smile, Bridget. Look at that hair, it's beautiful ... cutest little thing I've ever seen.' They stood for so long with the window between them that a fiery ache spread in Bridget's legs. She set Reynagh down in her crib and took the girls to a bench outside in the garden, where they could properly talk.

They sat on the bench for hours, happily chatting just like they used to back in London. Mary, Brenda, and Teresa told Bridget all the latest news from St Ann's – the nurses who had new boyfriends, the patients who'd come in with all sorts of diseases, the shenanigans from nights out in the West End. In turn, Bridget told the girls all about the gruelling birth, the other mothers she'd met in Epping Hospital, and the mother and baby home and its daily chores and nasty nuns. There was so much to fill each other in on. But there was one thing they didn't talk about. It was weighing on Bridget's mind, and she was sure it was weighing on theirs as well. The sound of wind in the trees filled a break in the conversation. It lingered as the girls sat around, staring at the ground and saying nothing. Teresa eventually broke the silence.

'So,' she said. 'What happens when you leave here?'

The three girls spun their attention towards Bridget, their gazes piercing into her in anticipation.

'I'm not sure,' Bridget replied.

'We still want to help,' Brenda said.

'Course we do,' Mary added.

Teresa put her arm around Bridget and said, 'Fook what the nuns here say. The oul bitches. We're here for ya, Bridget.'

'I know,' Bridget said. 'And that means the world to me.'

The silence resumed. Bridget looked at the girls' deflated expressions, which were now directed towards the ground. She suspected they'd all come to the same conclusion – the plan they'd come up with in her dorm room at St Ann's months earlier, the plan to raise Reynagh themselves, would never work.

THREE WEEKS TO GO

Sister Francis, the old nun based in the nursery, wasn't like the other nuns at the mother and baby home. Some of the unmarried mothers had no idea how to change a baby at first. But Sister Francis was always happy to demonstrate how it was done.

'Hold the legs up,' Sister Francis would say. 'Then wipe the baby, like this, no not that way, it's a girl, wipe the other way, wipe from fanny to arse, not arse to fanny. Now, once the little one is nice and clean, grab the fresh nappy. Through the legs. That's it. Very good. All clean now. Ye'll want to get used to doing that – ye'll have to do it again after breakfast.'

Some of the unmarried mothers were terrified to simply pick their child up. Their hands would tremble as they hovered them over the top of the baby in the crib, as though they were trying to build up the nerve to hold them.

'Don't be scared,' Sister Francis told them. 'Ye carried them for nine months. Ye can carry them now. Nice and gently, put your arms under the wee one and cradle it. Very good. Very good. Don't forget to support the head. Don't drop it now. We know what happens to babies who get dropped on their heads. They end up simple. And they're never the same again!'

Sister Francis would also always show interest in the newborns when they arrived back from the hospital.

'What a little blessing,' she'd say. 'What's the name? ... Oh, that's a lovely wee name. And how old is he ... Oh, it's a she. Lord above, forgive me, it's my old eyes. Well isn't *she* lovely. And how much did the little one weigh? Nine pounds! Ye poor thing. How are ye still standing?'

Who knows how many thousands of babies Sister Francis had seen pass through the nursery over the years. But she still did her best to make every unmarried mother feel like *their* child was special. She never looked down on the mothers either. It wasn't because of her short stature. It was because she was kind and compassionate. She restored Bridget's faith in the nuns at the home. And having been raised as a strict Catholic, faith was always important to Bridget.

'I'd like to get Reynagh baptised,' Bridget told the Reverend Mother after breakfast one morning. ''Twould be grand to do it before our six weeks runs out, Reverend Mother. I'd be so grateful if ye'd let me.'

The Reverend Mother's black beady eyes narrowed as she considered Bridget's request. The head nun wasn't in the habit of obliging demands from the unmarried mothers, so Bridget suspected 'no' was about to come from her dry, grey lips.

'Very well,' the Reverend Mother finally said. 'The child made may be born in sin, but tis no doing of the child itself. You may get it baptised.'

With the Reverend Mother on board, Bridget's only concern was finding a godmother for Reynagh. In a perfect world, she would have asked her sister, Maureen, to be the godmother of her firstborn child. But Maureen was out of reach at a convent in Australia. She didn't know Reynagh existed. And even if she did, there was no way Bridget could ask her. This was most certainly not the perfect world. So, Bridget decided to ask one of the unmarried mothers instead – a Polish woman named Nadzieja, whom Bridget had once seen praying beside her son's crib.

'Hiya, Nadzieja,' Bridget said, having approached her in the nursery after dinner. 'There's something I want to ask you.'

'Yes,' Nadzieja said in her uncertain Polish accent.

'I asked the Reverend Mother if I could get Reynagh, my little girl, baptised. And I was wondering ... well ... if you wouldn't mind being her godmother. Tis no bother if you don't want to. I would understand. I just saw you praying and all and knew you were Catholic. Well of course you are, being here and all ... a Catholic home. But as I said, tis no bother if you don't want to. I just thought it would be nice—'

'Yes,' Nadzieja cut in, smiling warmly. 'It is great honour.'

Nadzieja wrapped her arms around Bridget like a lifelong friend celebrating good news. A month earlier, they had been complete strangers. But now Nadzieja, this unknown woman from Poland, would forever be the godmother of Bridget's firstborn child.

On Sunday morning, just after six o'clock, Bridget carried Reynagh into the chapel. It was empty inside apart from Father Mooney and Nadzieja, who were both standing at the front altar.

Nadzieja's grin was still brimming, large and proud. Reynagh didn't cry as she was plunged into the icy-cold holy water. She didn't cry as Father Mooney poured the water over her head. And she didn't cry as Father Mooney proclaimed, 'I baptise you Reynagh in the name of the Father, the son, and the Holy Spirit.' The little girl just curiously looked around the chapel through her big brown eyes, most likely wondering why she was getting her morning bath in this place from an old man in white robes and not in the nursery from her mother. It was probably the quickest baptism Bridget had ever been to, lasting no longer than ten minutes. Bridget thanked Nadzieja (who had managed all of the responses in perfect English, despite her usually broken dialect) one final time. She left the chapel with a huge sense of relief, knowing that whatever happened in Reynagh's life, from this point onwards she would always be a Catholic in the eyes of Bridget's Lord.

TWO WEEKS TO GO

Mary, Teresa, and Brenda continued to visit as the days passed. And with those passing days, precious time diminished. They'd take it in turns making the trip from London to Epping on the days they weren't working. Almost every afternoon , one of them would come. They'd stand in the corridor outside the nursery, staring in at Reynagh, who was in Bridget's arms on the other side of the glass. Then they'd walk with Bridget through the grounds and fill her in on the latest gossip.

'I always cry on the train ride home,' Teresa admitted one day during a visit. 'So do Brenda and Mary. I'm sorry to tell ya, Bridget. But I just want you to know ... we share the pain with you. We feel for you.'

Bridget was lost for words. She in no way wished the pain

upon the girls. But the burden was so large, there was some strange comfort in knowing she wasn't carrying it entirely by herself.

It was a Saturday morning, two weeks before their time was up, when Bridget was called to the entrance hall, where there was a visitor waiting to see her. Bridget arrived, expecting to see Mary, Brenda, or Teresa. But it wasn't any of them. It was a short, red-headed woman with an abundance of freckles covering her face.

'Hiya, Bridget,' the woman said.

It took Bridget a moment to recognise her. 'Anna!'

Bridget had met Anna a year or so earlier at St Ann's General Hospital in London. Anna was also a young nurse from Ireland. But Bridget and Anna never had too much to do with each other in London. They'd say hello if they passed each other in the hospital corridor, but they were by no means close friends.

'How are ya?' Anna asked as Bridget stood frozen in front of her in the entrance hall.

'I'm grand,' Bridget said.

Silence. Bridget's thoughts were all over the place. *Word must have got around back in London. They must be all talking about it.* She didn't even expect her close friends to visit, so it was especially surprising to be visited by a colleague she wasn't particularly close with. Anna outstretched her arms and wrapped Bridget in a warm hug. It wasn't the sort of hug that acquaintances give each other. It was wonderfully tight, and it lingered for longer than a normal greeting hug. Anna released Bridget and smiled, but her eyelashes were damp.

'Is it alright if I see the baby?' she asked.

'Of course!' Bridget replied, leading her towards the nursery. She picked Reynagh up from her crib and carried her to the window that bordered the corridor, just as she did when she showed her off to Mary, Teresa, and Brenda. Anna's eyes were glued to Reynagh as though she couldn't look at anything else. She pressed her hands against the glass as tears rolled down her freckly face.

A half hour later, after showing Reynagh off to Anna, Bridget took her surprise visitor to a park bench in the grounds where they could have a chat.

'She's beautiful,' Anna said.

'Thank you,' Bridget replied. 'She really is.'

Anna stared ahead at the trees like a woman waiting for confession – solemn with an unescapable grief that she couldn't hold in any longer. 'I know it's hard for you,' she said. 'I had a baby as well.'

'Oh ... Anna ...' Bridget said, taken aback at the confession.

'I had to give him up for adoption,' Anna continued. 'They told me it was for the best. "The child needs a proper home with both a mother and a father who are married, not sinners." My mammy refused to talk about it. Even today, she doesn't mention it. My daddy just said, "We'll get it sorted." Yeah, they feckin' sorted it, alright. They had my little boy taken away. And they haven't mentioned him since. That was two years ago, Bridget ... You're the first person I've told.'

'Oh, I'm sorry,' Bridget said, placing her hand on Anna's.

'It's alright,' Anna said, wiping her eyes. 'The nuns told me to get on with me life. So that's what I've done. And you know what, Bridget? Life goes on. The child grows up and my life ... just goes on. I'm not allowed to cry for him, not allowed to miss him. I just have to carry on ... like everything's normal ... like he doesn't exist.'

She turned her teary eyes towards Bridget. 'It's the hardest thing, Bridget,' she continued. 'I can't imagine ever not hurting.

But I carry on. And you will too. We *have* to be strong, Bridget, you and I. Not for us ... for our babies.'

Bridget didn't know what to say. She'd barely known anything about Anna before today, even though they'd lived under the same roof in London for the past year. She had assumed Anna was just another young Irish nurse living the dream in London. There was certainly nothing to suggest that she had been forced to give up a child. She'd managed to hide it from everyone at St Ann's. She'd found a way to keep living, even though a part of her was missing. And she was still standing, she was still breathing, and she at least projected the image of happiness through her pleasant greetings in the hospital corridor. Anna had found a way to carry on after the greatest loss one could imagine.

Bridget just wasn't so sure she would be able to do the same.

ONE WEEK TO GO

The end was almost upon them. More than five weeks had passed. Once the sixth week ended, Bridget and Reynagh would no longer be welcome at the mother and baby home. Beyond the walls of the home was the wilderness – a sprawling mass of English countryside, villages and towns, and London itself in all its bustling glory. And among that vast wilderness, beyond the safety and comfort of the mother and baby home, there was nowhere for Bridget and Reynagh to go.

'Please, Lord,' Bridget prayed every night. 'Give me strength to give Reynagh the life she deserves. Look over her. Guide her. Please, Lord ... don't let her end up in Nazareth House. I beg you, Lord. Punish *me* for my sins, not her.'

Bridget received a phone call two days before her and Reynagh were due to be kicked out of the home.

'I'm sorry.' Her social worker Linda's voice came from the earpiece. 'I've tried everywhere, Miss Reilly. I've had no luck. I'm sorry it has to be this way. But there's no other option. The child will have to go to Nazareth House in London.'

Bridget almost dropped the phone right there on the spot.

'But I want you to know,' Linda continued, 'I won't stop looking. Finding parents is never easy. But it does happen. I've lost count of how many times I've made it happen.'

Bridget couldn't bring herself to talk. Her rapid, shallow breath was the only sound that ricocheted through the phone.

'It could be worse, Miss Reilly. At least your child will have a roof over her head. She'll be fed and clothed. She won't be alone. Nazareth House is not the worst place she could be, Miss Reilly.'

But to Bridget, it *was* the worst place she could be, and no amount of reasoning on Linda's part could change that. In her desperation, she sought a meeting with the Reverend Mother a day before the six weeks of tenancy expired.

'What do ye want?' the Reverend Mother snarled as Bridget entered her office.

Bridget's hands were clammy, her heart thudding heavily in her chest. The old nun in front of her was sitting behind a dark oak desk, her lips scrunched tight, her black beady eyes glaring (as they always did).

'What's the meaning of that long puss on ye face?' the Reverend Mother said, her nostrils flaring. 'Go on. Spit it out, girl. What do ye want?'

'I've had some news from my social worker, Reverend Mother,' Bridget answered softly.

'And?' she barked back.

'Well, she hasn't been able to find anywhere for my child to go.'

The Reverend Mother's expression didn't change. She appeared to be unmoved by the news.

'And my six weeks ends tomorrow,' Bridget continued, her cheeks burning from that persistent blushing. 'So ... Reverend Mother, I was wondering if you could perhaps let us stay a little while longer.'

The Reverend Mother leaned back in her chair, her wrinkled face tightening. 'Tell me, girl, what do ye see when ye go in the nursery?'

'My baby,' Bridget answered, wondering if it was a trick question.

'And what do ye see when ye look around the rest of the nursery?'

Bridget took a moment to answer, not wanting to be scolded for saying the wrong thing. 'I see other babies and their mothers.'

'Yes!' the Reverend Mother said. 'And do ye see any *empty* cribs in the nursery?'

'No,' Bridget answered softly.

'No. Ye don't see empty cribs in the nursery because we don't have the luxury of having empty cribs in the nursery. Tis full year-round. Tis full as long as stupid young girls like you let stupid young boys spoil their bodies in sin. The devil would be smiling in delight, seeing how packed our nurseries are.'

The Reverend Mother was spitting as she spoke. Some of the speckles of saliva had even landed on Bridget, but she was too polite to wipe them away.

'Jesus!' the Reverend Mother said, sighing before looking up at the small wooden crucifix on her wall. 'It boggles the mind how girls like you complain about your situation when ye have no one to blame but yourself. Think of our poor Lord on the cross up there on the wall ... with the crown of thorns on his head and the nails in his hands. How agonising that would have been for Christ our Lord! He did that for *you*. But for what? So ye could go and rub salt into his wounds by throwing away your purity? And now by your lack of gratitude for all we've done for ye. We've given you six weeks. And that will be all.'

Bridget tried to hold back tears. 'Please,' she said. 'Please, Reverend Mother. I've got nowhere else to take my little girl!'

'There are always places ye can take her,' the Reverend Mother said, casting her black beady eyes away from the crucifix and back onto Bridget.

'I can't put her in an orphanage!'

'Is that right?' the Reverend Mother, her voice sarcastically high-pitched. 'Well that is something ye should have thought about before ye got yourself in this situation. Let me tell ye something ... you and your baby are not special. There're naughty girls like you across the whole country. The whole of God's green earth, for that matter. Lord above, we don't have the room to house the lotta ya. What am I to do about it? Now take that sour puss off ye face and walk back out the way ye came.'

Bridget left the Reverend Mother's office with her final bit of hope shredded into pieces. She went to the nursery, where she cuddled Reynagh. In a matter of hours, the two of them would essentially be turfed onto the street. There were no loving parents waiting to take Reynagh in. Bridget couldn't take her back to the dorm room at St Ann's. And she couldn't take her to her mammy and daddy. There was only one option. The option Bridget had been dreading all along.

She treasured her final evening with Reynagh at the mother and baby home in Epping. One final day together as mother and daughter. Tomorrow, Reynagh would become an orphan.

CHAPTER TWELVE

LAST RESORT

Bridget and Reynagh were apart. And the divide between them was far greater than the short walk between the dorms and nursery that had separated them at the mother and baby home in Epping. They were both in London, but Bridget was now living back at the nurses' home at St Ann's General Hospital. Reynagh was in Nazareth House, a huge orange brick building in Hammersmith, standing four storeys high with white crosses sitting upon its roof. The building was overcrowded with orphans, big and small, all of whom had nowhere else to go. And now Reynagh was one of them. How had it come to this? Everything had been a blur to Bridget since she'd left Epping. It was a bad dream, but one she couldn't remember. And now, she'd woken up back in London, and her little girl was locked up in that horrible place. *How* had it come to this?

Bridget's social worker, Linda, insisted during her regular phone calls that she was still trying to find adoptive parents for Reynagh. But her words did little to ease Bridget's guilt. She carried it every moment of the day – a relentless tight stabbing sensation in her chest that rendered her incapable of sitting still or feeling any form of comfort at all. The image of Reynagh alone in her crib in the orphanage was always at the back of Bridget's eyelids. Every night as she lay in her bed at St Ann's, she sobbed uncontrollably. By the time she was finally able to fall asleep, her pillow was drenched with tears and the sun was about to come up. But there was one thought that kept Bridget going, one remaining glimmer of hope, one last resort that could save Reynagh from an orphaned life. The only thing was that in order to pursue it, Bridget would have to leave London.

'You hafta go, Bridget!' Teresa said, as the girls gathered in Bridget's dorm room one evening.

'She's right,' Mary added. 'Don't you be worrying about Reynagh. We'll be there for her.'

'We'll visit her every day,' Brenda said, placing her hand on Bridget's shoulder.

Leaving London without Reynagh went against every motherly instinct that had become entrenched within Bridget. It was hard enough living on separate sides of London and having their relationship reduced to *allocated visiting time* at the orphanage. But she knew the girls were right. She *needed* to leave London. It was her only hope to give Reynagh the life she deserved.

Bridget's mammy and daddy had moved back to Belmullet not long after her twenty-first birthday. They said they brought forward their return to Ireland because Bridget's sister, Maureen, was coming home for a visit, all the way from the convent in Australia. They wanted her to feel at home in the house she grew up in, not some townhouse in Bradford. But it would be Bridget and not Maureen whose homecoming would transpire first.

Bridget left London by train, then England by boat, before arriving in Dublin and boarding a bus to Belmullet. There was a long and rocky road ahead. At the end of it, she'd face her parents for the first time in months, and for the first time as a mother herself. The drive took her through countless towns and villages that became more familiar the closer she got to the west coast. She stared out the window at the never-ending sprawl of green fields, quaint pubs, little cottage homes and, of course, the grand churches, with their crosses towering above any other building in town. She had travelled along the same roads in the opposite direction four years earlier, when she had first left home as an eighteen-year-old. She was a different person back then, dreaming of life in the big city and all it would have to offer. But now all she could think about as the bus edged closer to her beloved Belmullet was her little girl, who was all alone in an orphanage in London. *Is she okay? Are the nuns properly looking after her? Has Linda found adoptive parents yet? Are the girls visiting her? Does she miss me? What will Mammy and Daddy say? Will they save us?* The questions swirled around Bridget's head, but no answers came to accompany them.

In Belmullet, everyone knew everyone. It was the sort of place where secrets were hard to keep. But everyone was in the business of keeping secrets (especially if the secret could affect the good standing of your family name). A life in Belmullet was a simple life. It was a life on the land, farming cattle and livestock, which were usually bought and sold at the monthly market in the main streets of town. It was a life on the water, reeling in vast stocks of fresh fish from the Atlantic Ocean. It was a life filled with traditional Irish music, not just from the scratchy sounds of record players, but also through live performances of the fiddle and flute, of which there were many players around town.

Singing was also a fixture in most households. But mainly it was heard at the local pubs, where the sounds of angelic voices and the strained chords of the intoxicated blared together in unison. A life in Belmullet was a life of staying put and not straying too far from the familiar surroundings of the west coast. It was a life of unbridled generosity and hospitality – whether bringing food to families who were mourning a loved one, or hosting an uninvited neighbour for tea and cake. But most of all, a life in Belmullet was a life for the Lord. *Everything*, good and bad, was spoken of in reference to the Lord.

'May the Lord have mercy on the poor man's soul.'

'Thank the Lord, she finally found herself a husband!'

'What an eejit! The stupid boy needs to ask the Lord's forgiveness for what he's done.'

'Jesus, Mary, and Joseph! The Lord musta been having a bad day when he created that one.'

Every action, every thought of everyone in Belmullet was done in the belief the Lord was watching. And as Bridget arrived back in town, she prayed he'd do more than just watch when she came face-to-face with her parents. Perhaps, she hoped, he could intervene.

'Ahh! Welcome home,' Bridget's mammy said as she walked up the front path, dragging her case behind her. Her mother was smiling – something Bridget hadn't seen during their last encounter in Bradford. Her mammy seemed to sneak a quick glance towards Bridget's belly, then back up to her face (or did Bridget imagine that?). The smile remained. Perhaps it was a smile of relief, Bridget thought – relief that she was neither pregnant nor holding a baby.

'I sure am glad to see ya,' her mammy continued. 'There's plenty of work to be done around here.'

And she was right. She had Bridget working straight away. Scrubbing the floors, washing the walls and then giving them a fresh lick of paint, dusting every reachable surface in the house, peeling vegetables and preparing lunch and dinner before cleaning the kitchen from top to bottom. Bridget's wrists ached and her knees were red raw, much like they were during her daily chores at the mother and baby home. The work at the Reilly household in Belmullet never seemed to stop. And neither did Bridget's racing mind. She kept rehearsing the speech in her head as she worked – how she would talk to her mother about Reynagh.

She's gorgeous, Mammy. She's your granddaughter. Surely you're wondering what she looks like? Surely you want to hold her in your arms? Please, Mammy, I've got nowhere to take her. She's stuck in a bloody orphanage in London. It's killing me, Mammy. I'm sorry for the shame I've brought upon you and the family, but I need your help. Reynagh needs your help. Please, Mammy. I'll clean every day, the entire house from top to bottom. I'll do anything, Mammy. Please help us. The words came easily to Bridget when they were only inside her head. Saying them aloud to her menopausal mother was a far more daunting prospect.

Three days passed, each of them filled with a never-ending list of chores. But beyond the back-breaking work, the days were immersed in painful silence. Bridget's pregnancy and the birth of Reynagh remained unspoken. But it felt that the conversation was never far away, as though it was stuck somewhere in the middle ground between their thoughts and their mouths. During dinner each night, as Bridget sat around the table with her mother and father, they spoke as they always had; they even joked and laughed. It was just like the way things had been before Bridget left for London several years earlier. But in between the chatting and the laughter, that familiar dreaded silence reared its head, and Bridget wondered – *will they bring it up now?* For three days, the answer was always the same – *no*. She knew it would be up to her to ask for help. She decided it was best to approach her mother and not her father. He would only do what her mother said anyway. It was her mammy's opinion, her decision, that would matter.

Tuesday morning after breakfast, Bridget was in the kitchen scrubbing grease off the stovetop with a thick steel brush. Her mammy was standing at the table behind her, peeling vegetables that had been picked from the garden that morning. She was humming and appeared to be in a good mood. Or perhaps it was relief in her demeanour – relief that Bridget hadn't yet mentioned anything about her baby, as though saying it aloud would bring it even further into existence. Bridget gripped the steel brush extra tight and tried to summon all her courage. This would be as good a time as any for her to confess, to repent, to beg for help.

'You wouldn't believe the news,' her mammy said as she worked away at the table.

Bridget stopped scrubbing and turned to her mother. 'What news?'

'Ye know the Quinns?' her mammy said. 'Well, something happened with their youngest. You know, the blonde one, Sinead.'

'Oh yes, I know Sinead.'

'A terrible thing happened.' Her mammy gasped. 'Her poor parents.'

Bridget feared she was about to be told of a horrible accident involving Sinead, or even worse, her tragic death. 'What happened?'

Her mammy stopped peeling spuds for a moment, gathering her thoughts. It took her a while to answer.

'Sinead went and got herself pregnant,' she finally said, her voice cold and harsh.

Bridget's muscles seized up, making her dead still. Realising how odd she must look, she hastily turned back towards the stovetop and continued scrubbing the grease away. Her mammy spoke again, filling the unnerving quietness. 'I mean, what was the stupid girl thinking? Her poor mother and father. I don't know how they'll cope.'

Bridget focused her gaze on the thick black grease in front of her. *Just scrub*, she told herself. A burning sensation swept across her face as her cheeks reddened, almost matching the tomatoes that had been picked from the garden and were now sitting on the table behind her. She kept scrubbing, harder and harder, faster and faster, even though her wrist was numb and her hands cramped like crab claws. Her mother kept talking behind her.

'Lord above. No mother or father should have to go through that. Especially such lovely people like them. Such good Catholics as well! The *shame* they must be feeling.'

Just keep scrubbing, Bridget kept telling herself as her steel brush clogged with grease from the stovetop.

'And now the poor parents have to look after the silly girl,' her mammy continued. 'Can ye believe that, Bridget? Even after all she's put them through. Even after disgracing the family name like that. Tis just awful.'

Bridget wanted to throw down the steel brush and yell at her mother. *The poor parents! What about Sinead? And her child? What about them? I bet you haven't thought about them, Mammy!* She felt a fire burning within her, an urge to scream, to speak up to her mother. She was clenching the steel brush so hard, her knuckles had turned white. But, as though incapacitated, that was all she could do. She couldn't trust herself to speak at this moment, mostly out of fear of what horrible words the fire within her would spark. So, she just scrubbed as her mother continued to berate the defenceless Sinead Quinn while pitying her *poor* parents.

'And now the mother and father have to ask themselves, "What are the neighbours saying about us?" Lord above, can ye imagine, Bridget? The embarrassment. The shame. Tis a terrible thing.'

Bridget kept cleaning the now spotless section of stovetop. But she noticed out of the corner of her eye that her mother was gently shaking her head, as if she was showing disapproval to a misbehaving toddler. Neither of them spoke another word to each other for the rest of the morning.

Bridget went walking in the fields later that day after all her chores were done. She sat on a rock, a few miles from home, and watched the sun set over the Atlantic Ocean. The last of the day's golden rays dipped over the horizon, giving way to the darkness. The blue sky quickly turned to black, as though a great big curtain that covered the earth was being pulled away. Stars began to appear in the darkening heavens. She lay back on the rock, her breath turning to mist as she watched the night sky come to life. Soon enough, it was covered in a splattering of stars. She'd missed this. She never got to see this in London, where a hazy blanket of light smothered the city at night. But as she gazed up at the glistening spectacle that she'd missed so much over the past three years, all she wanted was to be somewhere else. For the first time in her life, she didn't feel at home in Belmullet. For she knew there was no saviour for her and Reynagh to be found here. There was nothing here for them now. Nothing but shame.

She left the following day, alone and downtrodden. As the lumbering bus traversed the eastbound roads to Dublin, she reflected on her homecoming and what it meant for Reynagh. It was now clear there was only *one* option that could give Reynagh the life she deserved ... adoption. Bridget knew it was the only way. She barely had enough money to support herself in London; she certainly couldn't afford to raise a child as well. But adoption was no guarantee. Her social worker, Linda, still hadn't managed to find suitable parents. And every day she didn't call was another day Reynagh lived the orphan life. Bridget couldn't handle the thought of that continuing any longer, or even worse – becoming permanent. She prayed for most of the journey back to London, figuring that if her parents weren't going to help her, perhaps the Lord would.

Her first stop back in London was Nazareth House, where she found Reynagh in her crib, eyes red and face damp with tears.

'Shh,' Bridget said, lifting her into her arms. 'Your mammy's back now. Shh. I'm here, beautiful girl.'

In that moment, Bridget realised she had barely coped being apart from Reynagh for a few days. There was no way she could do it for a lifetime.

A nun eventually came into the nursery, interrupting the loving reunion. 'Miss Reilly,' she said. 'Your social worker's on the phone. She says she's been trying to reach you for days.'

Bridget rushed out of the nursery to pick the phone up.

'It's Linda here,' the voice came through the earpiece. 'I have some good news.'

Bridget's heart seemed to halt momentarily before it sprung to life again, pounding heavily in her chest.

'We've found them!' Linda said. 'And they're just what we're looking for. They're older. In their thirties. And they already have kids. But they want another girl. Miss Reilly, they want *your* girl.'

Bridget's grip on the phone loosened, and her legs became unsteady as a collision of dread and relief crashed into her. In a way, her prayers had been answered in that moment. Reynagh could now be given a proper upbringing, with loving parents and brothers and sisters. But that also meant saying goodbye and not being allowed to contact her. It meant waiting for Reynagh to reach adulthood and track her down, or possibly never seeing her again. It was a bittersweet revelation. A sudden shot to her chest of ecstasy and agony. The soaring heights of love and the crippling depths of despair were engulfing Bridget at the same time. But as she stood there in the orphanage on weary legs with the phone pressed to her ear, she knew this was the *only* way.

She was allowed one more visit the following day. It would be her final chance to say goodbye. She held Reynagh in her arms in the orphanage nursery, marvelling down at her. Reynagh was so small, so delicate and precious. Her head was covered in a thick mop of jet-black hair. Her big brown eyes curiously looked up while her tiny hands gripped around her mother's finger. Bridget could feel the gentle tapping of Reynagh's beating heart against her own chest. She still couldn't believe that she had created this life that was within her grip. Sure, she'd held babies before, but it didn't compare to this. Growing up in Belmullet, when someone in town gave birth, Bridget would sometimes get to hold the little bundle of joy when it was passed around like a new toy. She'd also held babies while nursing at St Ann's. She sometimes used to wonder when she'd be holding her own little one. And now here she was, a world away from home, holding *her* baby girl, and she couldn't have been more perfect.

She combed her fingers through Reynagh's thick black hair. It was soft and silky to the touch. She imagined how those locks would grow and one day flow down past Reynagh's shoulders. Perhaps it would lose its straightness and eventually form natural curls like Bridget's hair. Maybe as an adult Reynagh would grow her hair down to her waist, so it could bounce when she walked and glisten in the sun. Or maybe she'd cut it real short, so it wouldn't cover any of her beautiful face. She spent several minutes combing her little girl's hair, wondering what it would one day turn into, because she knew she would never get the chance to find out.

Reynagh's pursed lips curled into a smile as she gawked up at her mother. She seemed blissfully oblivious to the troubles of the world. She had no idea what lay ahead for her. And really, neither did Bridget, and that's what terrified her most.

She had been standing by Reynagh's crib for close to two hours. Her back throbbed and toes tingled with an unshakeable numbness as she stood, child in arm. It began to dawn on her that she'd be forced to leave in just a few minutes when *allocated visiting time* came to an end. And that meant it would be time to say goodbye. Her little girl, cuddled in her arms, would soon have to leave this place for good. Her new life was waiting. And no matter how much it hurt, Bridget couldn't be a part of that life.

'I'll always love you, Reynagh,' Bridget whispered.

She knew her child didn't understand her – she was barely three months old. But she kept talking, hoping the words would miraculously one day return to Reynagh in her dreams.

'I'll always have a special place in my heart for you. I'm so sorry.' She struggled to say the words aloud. 'I wish I could keep you. But it has to be this way. You deserve a better life.'

A few droplets fell on Reynagh's white robes. It took Bridget a moment to realise they were from her. Tears were welling in her eyes. And she feared Reynagh would see those tears and somehow also see the unrelenting sadness behind them. She pulled Reynagh closer to her body and embraced her in a motherly hug. Reynagh's little head rested on her shoulder, and her soft breath caressed her neck. Bridget glanced out beyond Reynagh's crib at the rest of the room. About a dozen other cribs filled the nursery. In each there was a baby, each of them just a few months old. But no one stood beside them. They were all alone in their own little world, confined to their tiny beds, each of which were surrounded by black metal bars – a tiny prison for a tiny human. Some children stirred in their beds, rustling their sheets as they stretched out their little arms and legs. Some of the babies softly cried as their eyes darted around the room, as though searching for their mothers and fathers. Some quietly slept, while others roared and squealed like an infant that's just entered the world. All the babies were dressed in white robes that hung down past their feet (most likely so they could grow into them). With its old wooden floorboards and high ceilings, the room had a chill about it, a certain iciness hanging in the air. There was no sunshine coming through the large rectangular windows – just the greyish haze of a gloomy sky. Bridget worried about Reynagh and the other children being cold with just a little white blanket to cover them. But more than that, she worried about what lay ahead for the little ones. Whether they were born out of wedlock or their parents were simply unable to raise them, the babies all faced uncertain futures. Bridget wanted to take Reynagh home with her more than anything. But she would have taken *all* the newborns home if she could. They didn't deserve to start their lives like this. Nazareth House in London wasn't only full of little ones who had just come into the world; there were also older kids. Children who were old enough to know where they were and what they were missing in their lives. But there was no love, no compassion within its walls. The nuns certainly didn't allow anything like that. It was a cold and clinical place, and Bridget hated that Reynagh had ever entered its doors.

A loud creak sounded through the nursery. Bridget turned to see a set of large wooden doors opening. One of the nuns appeared in the doorway, covered head to toe in black robes with just her face popping out of her habit. The old nun cleared her throat and stared at Bridget while holding the door ajar. Bridget knew what this look meant – it was time to leave. She turned away from the nun and kissed Reynagh on her forehead. She held her tight to her body again, not wanting to let go. This was the moment she had been dreading for so long. She kissed her again, this time on the head and on those luscious black locks. A creak sounded through the room once more as the nun pushed the door open slightly wider.

Bridget lifted Reynagh over the metal railing and began lowering her back into the crib. But she suddenly couldn't lower her any further. She pulled her back up again, bringing her in close to her chest as though the two were magnetically drawn to each other and unable to be pulled apart. She held her for a moment before the nun cleared her throat again, much louder than before. Bridget lifted Reynagh over the railing again and lowered her into the cot. She tucked the sheets over her tiny body, fearing she would get cold without the warmth of someone holding her.

'Miss Reilly!' the nun said. 'It's time.'

Bridget wrapped her fingers around the cold metal railing and lowered her head to Reynagh's face, kissing her one final time. 'I'm so sorry.'

As she pulled herself upright, her tears fell, sprinkling

Reynagh's tiny blanket. She slowly unclenched her grip on the railing and turned away, moving back towards the nun. With each second that passed, it became harder for Bridget to keep moving, as though she'd just been drugged with a fast-acting, paralysis-inducing substance. The old nun pulled the door back wide enough for Bridget to exit. But she didn't want to. She stopped in the doorway and turned her gaze back towards the room of parentless babies. Reynagh's face was still visible through the black metal bars of the crib. She was curiously looking over towards Bridget and the nun, not knowing this would be the last time she'd see her mother. The nun began closing the large wooden doors and Bridget was forced to step through them, cutting out her final glimpse of Reynagh's big brown eyes.

Bridget's leg muscles tightened as she descended the stairs towards the exit of Nazareth House, almost to the point she couldn't move. Her heart was breaking. With each step, it broke into another piece. A gaping hole in her life was tearing open, and it got bigger every time she set one foot in front of the other. She stepped outside the orphanage, and her face and bare hands were hit by the stinging chill of the London air. The large wooden door closed behind her. She took a step. *What sort of mother am I?* Another step. *I'll never see her again.* Another step. *I have no choice.* Another step. *She'll at least be loved.* Another step. *She'll have a nice home and nice parents and brothers and sisters to play with.* Another step. *She'll be happy.* Another step. *We'll always have our special bond.*

The tightness in Bridget's legs intensified with every stride, as did the stabbing of her chest and swirling of her stomach. She figured it was the feeling of guilt piercing into her, swarming within, where it would eventually fester. And she knew she'd never be rid of it. Nazareth House cast a shadow over her as she walked away. The outline of the crucifix projected darkness on the ground in front of her, as though God himself was casting judgement. She kept walking, not knowing what was next or how she would ever be whole again.

CHAPTER THIRTEEN

THE MEETING

'Time to put this unpleasantness behind you.' That's what a nun at the orphanage had told Bridget before her final goodbye. She'd said it so calmly as well, so casually, as though it really was that simple, as though it was going to be easy for Bridget to relinquish her firstborn child then simply get back to work and pretend the past year had never happened. But Bridget knew that would never happen, and that now-empty chasm in her life could never be filled. *I'll never see her again* – that was her only thought in the days after the farewell, as though it was stitched into the fabric of her mind.

Bridget did her best to return to life as it was before she fell pregnant. She went to work each day on the wards of St Ann's. She spent her nights in the common room at the nurses' home, blankly staring at the TV screen before retreating to the darkness of her dorm and the comfort beneath her sheets. Life was once again monotonous. Monotonously empty. A week passed before

Bridget heard from Linda again. She called the nurses' home one night just after dinner.

'I'm calling about the adoptive parents,' Linda said. 'They want to see you!'

One week later, Bridget sat on the train as it passed through the countryside on its northbound journey. But she wasn't alone. Mary, Brenda, and Teresa were sitting in the carriage alongside her. Bridget couldn't sit still. Her foot was tapping fretfully, her fingers clenching the coarse fabric of the seat, her eyes darting all over the place. But she wasn't saying anything. None of them were. No words were needed. The girls' presence was all the support Bridget needed. Time seemed to drag along slowly, far slower than the lumbering carriages along the tracks. Her mind was solely focused on what was to come in the hours ahead. The trouble was, she wasn't entirely sure what that would consist of.

Three hours passed before the train came to a steadying halt, but Bridget's anticipation did not. The girls disembarked the train with dozens of other passengers. They made their way across the platform, past a sign with 'Nottingham' written on it. Bridget led the way up the stairs and out onto the street. They stood beneath the towering orange blocks of the station and the large old-fashioned clock perched upon it. It hadn't yet ticked past 9 a.m., which meant they had more than one hour to find their destination. Bridget led the way down the street with the girls marching behind, either side of her. The shy young girl who used to follow was no more. Bridget was now a woman, leading. She had gone over the directions dozens of times before leaving London. But still she worried. *What if we get lost? We can't be late. We have to find it. What if we don't find it?*

After about twenty minutes of walking up and down the surrounding streets, and asking several locals for directions, they arrived at their destination. It was a dreary brown building, standing four storeys high, with just the number 275 plastered on the front in faded gold. There was no other signage. It was the sort of building you could walk past every day for years on end and still have no idea what happened inside. Bridget stopped in front of the building, casting her head back to look up at the dull concrete façade, her heart fluttering and breath shortening. She felt the warm touch of hands upon her shoulders. The girls were huddling around her.

'You can do this, Bridget,' Teresa whispered in her ear.

'We're right here with ya,' Mary added.

'That's right,' Brenda said. 'Right behind ya.'

Bridget inhaled deeply and opened the front door, leading the girls through it. They started climbing a narrow wooden staircase that creaked with every step. It had none of the polish or grandeur of the forbidden staircase at the mother and baby home. These stairs were well-worn and looked like they'd been trodden on daily for many years. She could feel herself becoming light-headed as she climbed, her vision darkening around the edges. Just before they reached the fourth floor, her foot slipped and she fell forward. She barely managed to put her hands in front of her face before it crashed into the steps. She gasped, then reached her sweaty palms towards the railing and pulled herself upright, trying to gather her composure. Her face was now burning, her cheeks bright red. She straightened out her jacket and skirt and wiped her brow, but accepted she would have to make this first impression while looking like a flustered mess. On the fourth floor, they found a woman in her forties sitting behind a desk.

'Hello,' Bridget said, her voice broken and shaky. 'I'm Bridget Reilly ... I have an appointment.'

'Miss Reilly,' the woman said. 'I didn't know you'd be bringing anyone. Who have we got here?' The woman glared at Mary, Brenda, and Teresa.

'Ah ... these are my friends,' Bridget said. 'We work together in London ... they're like my family.'

The woman's glare didn't relent, and Bridget thought she was about to kick them out, back down the stairs she'd just almost face-planted.

'Very well,' the woman finally said, getting to her feet. 'But you must know, Miss Reilly, this is a very unusual situation. We don't normally allow contact at this stage of the process. I certainly can't recall ever facilitating any meetings like this. But the adopted mother was very insistent.'

They followed the woman into an adjoining room. Bridget's heart was pounding feverishly, each thud reverberating in her ears like a booming drum. In the next room, there was another woman in her mid-thirties, wearing a bright green suit. She was sitting behind a table in an otherwise bare space. An empty pram was alongside her. A baby was sitting on her knee. But it wasn't just a baby: it was Reynagh, wide awake and smiling. Bridget couldn't take her eyes off her little girl, who wasn't nearly as little as the last time she had seen her. She seemed so much bigger, her black hair thicker and longer, even though it had only been a matter of weeks.

'Go on, Miss Reilly, sit down,' the woman from the front desk said. 'Debra, this is Bridget. And these are her nursing friends, if you're happy for them to be here?'

The woman in the green suit with Reynagh on her knee, Debra, nodded obligingly. She held her hand out to greet Bridget, who shook it, looking her in the eye so as not to be rude, even though she didn't want to take her eyes off Reynagh. Mary,

Teresa, and Brenda gave Debra a wave and then sat down in chairs against the wall behind Bridget.

'Okay,' the woman from the front desk said. 'I'm going to leave the room now. I'm sure you have a lot of questions for each other. Debra ... let me know when you're done.' She left the room, shutting the door behind her.

The room fell silent.

'That's a lovely green suit,' Bridget said.

Debra chuckled, twirling her brown hair through her fingers. Her cheeks also were tinged with little red blotches. It struck Bridget that Debra was nervous as well, perhaps as nervous as she was.

'Thank you,' Debra said, revealing her soft English accent. 'I actually wore this because they told me you were Irish. I don't know ... I thought it would be fitting, I guess.'

Bridget smiled, appreciating the gesture. Her eyes were then drawn back down to Reynagh, who was gently bouncing up and down on Debra's knee. 'I can't believe how big she is.'

'Do you want to hold her?' Debra asked.

It was the question Bridget had been waiting to hear. 'I'd love to!'

Debra carefully lifted Reynagh off her knee and handed her to Bridget. She was slightly heavier than Bridget remembered, but just as cute. Bridget rested the little girl on her knee, just as Debra had been doing. And then she took a moment to simply enjoy the warmth of her touch, the smell of her skin, the sounds of her little murmurs and baby grunts, and the sight of her big brown eyes curiously looking up at her.

'How has she been sleeping?'

'She sleeps well,' Debra said. 'Not always at night, though. We've been getting up to her in the early hours of the morning.

Me and my husband Rob, that is. I'm sorry he can't be here today. He just thought … it would be better if it was just the two of us.'

'That's okay,' Bridget said.

'Reynagh has her daddy wrapped around her little finger,' Debra went on. 'No doubt he'll spoil her when she gets older. It's funny how men aren't so tough any more when they have to answer to their little girl.'

It was nice for Bridget to hear that Reynagh would be looked after so well, even if it meant she wouldn't be the one to do it.

'I like the name Reynagh, by the way,' Debra said. 'So does Rob, and our other kids as well. So we decided to keep it. I hope that's okay.'

'Of course,' Bridget said, smiling, a sense of pride swelling in her. 'Your other children. Are they …'

Debra found the words to finish Bridget's question, just as she started to regret asking it. 'Did *I* give birth to them?' Debra said. 'Yes, I did. It's okay to ask. But I want you to know, Rob and I consider Reynagh to be *our* child as much as the others.'

'And how are they with Reynagh? Your other children?'

The question brought an instant smile to Debra's face. 'They love her,' she said. 'My youngest boy was so excited when we brought her up from London, he ran out to the car and pulled the back door open before it came to a stop. Just so he could get a glimpse of her. She was part of the family straight away.'

Bridget felt a tingling across her body, the hairs on her neck and arms standing up as she bounced Reynagh on her knee. Her prayers had been answered. Reynagh had the family she deserved. She would grow up as a beloved daughter and sister. She knew that now, without even the faintest bit of doubt. But still, she had so many questions for Debra.

'And how has she been feeding?'

'Very well,' Debra said. 'Like clockwork actually. Just look at the little tummy, poking out.'

Bridget laughed as she combed her fingers through Reynagh's hair. It was just as soft and silky as she'd remembered. There was just a whole lot more of it now.

'It's grown so much,' she said, admiring the shiny black locks that now covered most of Reynagh's little ears.

'That was the first thing we noticed when we saw her,' Debra said. 'We fell in love with her straight away. Couldn't be happier.'

'She seems happy too,' Bridget said before silence crept into the room again. She had so many more questions she wanted to ask. She wanted to know *everything* that had been happening in Reynagh's life, no matter how small or trivial it might have seemed. But she knew time was limited in this meeting. And there was one question she simply couldn't leave out.

'Can I ask something of you?' Bridget said. 'To make a promise. It would just mean the world to me if you could ... please ... tell Reynagh that I love her ... and I've always loved her. And I'll never stop loving her.'

'Of course,' Debra said with absolute sincerity.

'Thank you,' Bridget said. 'And there's one more thing ...'

Bridget's voice cut out. She was choking up amid an impending sadness attached to the words she was about to mutter. 'Please ...' she continued. 'Just let her know ... that I'm *sorry*. I didn't want it to be this way. But I can't give her the life she deserves.'

'I'll let her know,' Debra said.

'Thank you,' Bridget said, wiping away her tears, which were coming out like a leaky faucet.

'You don't need to thank me. You've given us the best gift anyone could give another person. Thank *you*.'

'I'm glad Reynagh will have such a wonderful mother,' Bridget said. 'And family as well. I'm sure Rob and your other children are just as lovely.'

Debra smiled, her eyes drifting down to Reynagh on Bridget's lap. And that's where they stayed as she spoke.

'You're probably wondering why I asked to meet you here,' she said. 'The social workers said it was a bad idea. But I had to ...' She paused, as though unable to find the words to continue. 'I want to make sure,' she went on, 'that *you* are sure. I didn't want you regretting it and wanting to get her back. I don't know. I thought it was best to meet with you, face-to-face, to make sure you don't have any doubts.'

Bridget noticed that Reynagh was looking over at Debra, reaching her arms out towards her like any child reaching for their mother.

'I want the best for my little girl,' Bridget said, wiping her tears again. 'I wish ... more than anything ... that I could give it to her. But I can't. *You* can.'

Debra exhaled, appearing relieved, but trying not to show it. 'Thank you,' she said, smiling at Bridget. Bridget did her best attempt at a return smile, despite the tears drenching her face. Suddenly, the foul stench of a soiled nappy hit their nostrils.

'Somebody needs a change,' Debra said. 'Shall I take her?'

Bridget lifted Reynagh off her knee to hand her back over to her adoptive mother.

'Or,' Debra said, 'would you like to do it?'

'Oh, yes,' Bridget said. 'I'd love to.'

She placed Reynagh on the table alongside the soon-to-be-signed documents that would permanently divide them. The baby's big brown eyes stared upwards as Bridget lifted her legs and removed the old nappy. She'd become much better at changing nappies during her time at the mother and baby home, where she'd done it every day and where the old nun Sister Francis was always yelling out tips on how to do it properly. To most people, changing a nappy may have seemed like a menial task, even off-putting or just plain disgusting. But to Bridget, this was so much more than that. It was a moment to cherish. And cherish it did as she changed Reynagh on that table, knowing it would be the last time she'd ever do it.

'Looks like you've done that before,' Debra said.

Bridget finished up and lifted Reynagh off the table, cradling her in her arms.

'I'll give you the room,' Debra said, getting to her feet. 'I'm sure you want a bit of privacy to say goodbye.'

She left the room. Reynagh's eyes widened as she looked towards the closed door Debra had just walked through. Her mouth opened wide, producing a soft whimper at first and then a high-pitched scream. She was wailing, uncontrollably, inconsolably.

'Shhh,' Bridget said, rocking her back and forth, trying to calm her, just as she had when the husbands used to visit at Epping Hospital. But the cries wouldn't die down. Not this time.

'She's forgotten me,' Bridget said.

Mary, Teresa, and Brenda gathered around, placing their hands on Bridget's shoulders.

'Don't be silly,' Brenda said. 'She's hasn't forgotten you.'

'Course she hasn't,' Teresa said. 'She's a wee baby. Babies cry. That's what they do.'

'No, it's okay,' Bridget said. 'She knows I'm not her mammy any more.'

With the girls gathered around her, Bridget continued to rock Reynagh in her arms, trying to calm her down. Her cries gradually faded, but her big brown eyes aimed longingly in the direction of Debra. When she did look away, towards Bridget and the girls, the whites in her eyes were red and glassy. She looked at the adults in front of her as though they were strangers. She wriggled and squirmed in Bridget's arms, trying to break free, yearning for Debra, whose face must have become familiar to her. Bridget's own child was looking at her as though she was an outsider – a woman who had taken her away from Debra's familiar presence. But Bridget knew there were only a few minutes before their time together would be over for good. Those few minutes were not enough time to waste feeling sorry for herself. So she savoured them, every moment of them. Her final precious minutes with her little girl in her grasp. And when she heard the sound of the door creaking behind her, she accepted that their time together as mother and daughter was over. It had already ended, in fact, before this meeting even began. It ended the moment Debra had taken Reynagh home from Nazareth House in London. Since then, Debra had been 'Mum', a title she would forever hold.

Reynagh's crying stopped when Debra entered the room. The little girl's face lit up as she stretched her arms out towards the woman in the bright green suit. Bridget gave Reynagh a gentle kiss on the forehead before handing her over to Debra. Reynagh nestled in to Debra's body, her face digging into her shoulder.

'I suppose it's time,' Debra muttered softly, almost apologetically.

Reynagh was smiling as Debra held her. She wasn't wriggling around any more or trying to break free. She was so still, so comfortable, so content in her new mother's arms. Bridget had never seen her look as happy as this. Certainly not in the orphanage or the mother and baby home. Bridget gripped Debra and Reynagh in an all-encompassing hug. Two mothers, about to set off in completely different directions, holding each other, with their little girl between them. Letting go would send both women off on opposite trajectories – for one a life of incompleteness and uncertainty, for the other a life with a beautiful child. They held each other for a few minutes, consumed in the warmth of each other's touch and the love within it. Finally, but regretfully, Bridget released her grip, and in doing so let go of her little girl for the final time. Reynagh was still smiling, still glowing in Debra's arms. That image alone gave Bridget all the strength she needed to turn around and walk away. This time for good.

PRESENT

CHAPTER FOURTEEN

BOUND TOGETHER

I stare at his name, etched in gold on the glistening granite tombstone, which is speckled with hints of emerald green.

'Forever loved. Forever missed.'

Lying under this great big chunk of rock, several metres into the gravelly earth, is my father, John Patrick Donnelly. Fake flowers, faded under the scorching sun, fill two vases on the ground on either side of the headstone, which stands out against the bright orange gravel. It's quiet here in Wooroloo, about an hour from Perth, where I spent the early part of my childhood. The sun breaks through the cloud, cutting slithers of golden light through the trees, which fall upon me and warm my face. The wind picks up. I hear it first, rustling in the high grass of a nearby field. Then it arrives, swaying the branches above. It's strangely peaceful out here at the Wooroloo Cemetery, despite all the unavoidable reminders of death. But it's quiet, which is an unknown pleasure for a city-dweller like myself. That's why this is the only place I can truly talk aloud to Dad these days. It's stupid, I know. The notion of life after death has been lost on me for years – my entire adult life in fact. But still I come here and talk out loud to my dead dad. It's as though I'm clinging on to hope my agnostic logic is wrong, and he does in fact still exist in some form somewhere, and wherever that is, he can hear me. It's stupid, I know.

I used to come here every day after Dad died, as though visiting his grave regularly would make up for all the times I didn't see him when he was alive. These days I don't visit as much. Every few months or so. But I've got a lot to say during this particular visit.

'I'm writing a book with Mum,' I say. 'It's about her time in London when she fell pregnant. Mum wants to get the story out there ... to help other unmarried mothers. So she asked me to help write the story. I dunno. It's kind of ... *consuming* me at the moment. It's doing my bloody head in, to be honest. It's all I can think about.'

I pull out some pages of the manuscript that I'd recently printed. It's the part of Mum's story when she meets with Debra at the adoption agency – the last time Mum saw Reynagh as a baby. I read the words aloud to Dad as though he is listening and will give me feedback when I finish. But after I say the final word, the wind dies down and there's nothing but silence.

'Well, thanks for listening, Dad. Love ya.'

I return to my car and hit the road. It's about a one-hour drive back to my apartment in the city. I spend the journey thinking about my old man and whether he has a part to play in Mum's story.

Practically all of my childhood memories featuring Dad take place before I turn six. In the first few years of my life, I remember things being good. Dad plays outside with me and my brother and sister when he gets home from work. Sometimes we go camping on weekends and during the summer months. Sometimes he lets me sit on his motorbike with him when he rides down to the shops. He makes me laugh with his jokes and his impersonations. He is my dad – the father. But that quickly changes around the time I start pre-primary as a five-year-old, or rather I start *noticing* him changing. Dad always seems to be angry, shouting from the shed, shouting at us, shouting at Mum. He and Mum fight a lot. He constantly flies off the handle and yells his lungs out before taking off in his ute, the tyres throwing up gravel and dust in his wake. It gets to the point when I dread the moment he comes home from work in the afternoon, or when I hear him coming in from the pub long after my bedtime.

One day, when I'm still about five years old, he says to me, 'I'm going away on a little holiday. I won't be far away. Just up the road. You can still come and see me when you want.' But I barely see Dad in the years that follow. Whenever I do, it's a passing encounter at the supermarket, or when he turns up to my primary school and yells at staff, demanding to see us kids. I feel the same during each of these encounters. Drowning in panic. All the years of yelling, of apparent never-ending anger, have made me scared of him. Katy and Sean say they feel just the same. Still, Mum always asks if we want to see Dad. She says it's *our* decision, entirely ours. She just wants to protect us and make sure we don't get hurt. But we always say no, we're too frightened to see him. Dad then blames Mum, saying she's turned us against him. But that's not true. Our fear of Dad is because of Dad, and Dad alone. But he just can't see that.

More years pass. And I don't have a proper conversation with Dad until I'm fifteen years old. My older sister, Katy, is first to rekindle a relationship with him, then my brother, Sean. They tell me that Dad's asking about me – how I'm doing in school, how football has been going, what my hobbies are, all that sort of stuff. He's always asking to see me, apparently. Even though so much time has passed, I still get struck with that sense of panic when he's mentioned. I don't know if I want to see him again. Most of my memories of him remind me of that scared little boy I used to be in his presence. I don't want to be like that ever again. I'm almost a man now. So I can stand up to him. I can fight him if I need to. But maybe that's over the top. Maybe I should give him a chance. Who knows, maybe he's changed.

We arrange to meet at my sister's house. I get there early and wait in the lounge room, my leg twitching from the nerves. There's a rustling at the door and then a knock. Katy opens the door, revealing Dad standing there. He looks just like I remember him, apart from a few more greys above his ears and a bit of extra padding around his waist. But I'm slightly taller than him now. He hugs Katy and then shuffles in my direction. He's fidgeting with his hands; his eyes are darting all over the place. But he can't seem to look directly at me. He reaches out his arms and hugs me. He's crying on my shoulder. We release the hug and there's an awkward silence. 'It's good to see you,' he finally says in that low quiet voice, the sort of voice men use when they're trying to stop themselves blubbering like a child.

Over the next few years, Dad and I slowly build our relationship from scratch. It starts with a few more meetings at Katy's place. Then we start speaking on the phone occasionally as well. Then Sean and I start meeting up with him, every few weeks or so. We go to his house mostly, where we sit around, drinking tea, or beer, and chatting away. Dad even comes to watch me play footy. It's what I'd always wanted but never had – a father to do fatherly things with. After years of being absent from each other's lives, we're finally forming a proper relationship. I haven't forgotten the bad times, but I'm older now, and Dad doesn't seem nearly as angry and messed up as he used to be. He plans to take me to Ireland when I turn eighteen. It'll be my first time outside of Australia. It will also be a great opportunity to bond with Dad, to make up for some of the lost time.

But before that happens, *everything* changes. Dad rings me a few weeks before Christmas in 2007. We discuss a job he's arranged for me for the summer holidays. I've just finished my final year of high school and I need money before I start my studies at university. Dad got me a job with the local council, who've employed him as a truck driver for the last thirty years. I will be doing some sort of physical labour, like digging holes, or picking up rubbish, or holding a sign to warn motorists about upcoming roadworks. Whatever it is, I'm happy to do it. I need the money. Plus, I'll be working close to my dad. It will be another good chance for more of that father–son bonding stuff that we'd missed out on for so many years. So, we're speaking on the phone about the job and he asks, 'Can you put Sean on?' I lower the phone from my ear, find my brother and hand it to him. I don't say, 'Goodbye.' I don't say, 'Thanks for getting me the job, Dad. I'm really looking forward to working with you.' I definitely don't say, 'I love ya, Dad.' I just hand the phone over to Sean. Conversation over.

A couple of weeks later, I'm at a Christmas gathering with a few friends. It's the twenty-first of December. After a great night of laughter, drinks, and Christmas dinner with all the trimmings, there's a phone call to the house of the party host, about 11 p.m. It's Mum, and she asks for me to come home. It's a bit unusual for Mum to ring the party host instead of my own mobile. Maybe she thinks I'm driving and doesn't want me to answer the phone and take my eyes off the road. She is a worrier like that. So I don't think much of the call. I drive home. When I get there, I notice something odd. Sean's car is in the driveway, but Mum's is not. Where the bloody hell could she have gone in the time between her phone call and me arriving home? At this late hour as well? Something's not right.

I open the front door and come face-to-face with Sean. His eyes are red and puffy. 'Daniel,' he says in a shaky voice, his jaw quivering. 'Dad's been in an accident.'

'What?' I say. 'W-what do you mean?'

'He was hit by a car,' he says. 'Dan ... he died.'

Shock is the first thing that hits me. It engulfs my whole body – it's a weird tingling sensation. Then there's the disbelief. *What? No, that can't be right! Sean's just made a mistake. Dad's not dead.* Then, there's the guilt – *I should have said goodbye to him on the phone the other day. I should have made more of an effort to see him over the years. He didn't deserve to die alone.* All of these stages of grief come within the first minute or so, one after another. Sadness hasn't hit me yet, though. It's not real enough to be sad about right now. I guess that will come later.

Mum returns home soon after. She's been at Katy's place, delivering the news. Out of the three of us, Katy was closest with Dad. I bet she's inconsolable right now. A few minutes later, she arrives, looking just as distraught as I imagined. We all share hugs and shed tears before piling into Mum's car and heading to the hospital, where we have to formally identify Dad's body.

'I'm doing it,' Mum says. 'And no arguing. I'm not letting you see him like that.'

At the hospital, Katy, Sean, and I sit in the waiting room of the emergency department while Mum is taken downstairs to the morgue. Mum has actually worked at this hospital for years in the orthopaedic ward, several floors up. I'm not sure how she'll be able to return to this building and work every day with the memory of what she's about to see. She re-joins us in the waiting room within half an hour. Her lips are clamped shut, her eyes drawn away from us. She doesn't say anything. She doesn't need to. She's just seen Dad for the first time in years – the man she once loved and had three children with. But she saw him lifeless, cold and lying on a table. Katy keeps saying she wants to see him as well.

'No! You're not seeing him like that!' Mum says, holding back tears.

A few days later, we find out the driver of the car that hit Dad was blind drunk. More than three times over the legal blood alcohol limit, in fact. My despair turns to anger. But at least now there's someone to blame. It's the drunk driver's fault I'll never work with Dad in the summer holidays. It's the drunk driver's fault that Dad and I won't go on that trip to Ireland together. It's the drunk driver's fault that Dad will never have the chance to make amends with Mum. But there's something I can't blame the drunk driver for – all the years that were missed. All that time that Dad and I didn't see each other. Guilt festers within me. I should have gone to see him, even if I was scared of him, even if I was just a little kid, even if he was angry at the world. I should have tried to fix him. Maybe he could have changed earlier. Maybe he could have been a dad to me, like all my friends' dads were to them. Maybe everything would be different and he wouldn't be dead right now.

About a week after Dad died, we go to a chapel where we will have the final viewing of his body, followed by a rosary. The funeral director is eating KFC at her desk when we arrive. How can she eat that when there's a dead body in the next room? She wipes the chicken grease from her hands and takes us into the chapel where Dad is. Mum leads the way as Katy, Sean, and I walk down the aisle towards the front altar. The dark oak coffin is sitting there, dead centre. The top part of it is open, revealing a tiny profile glimpse of Dad's face. We slowly approach, taking one small step at a time. Mum gets to the coffin first and lets out a loud gasp. She turns to Katy, Sean, and me and stretches out her arms to shield our view, much like she used to when covering the television during inappropriate scenes when we were little kids.

'No,' she says. 'You don't have to look.'

We tell her it's okay. We can do this. We're strong enough. We approach the coffin and Dad's face comes into view. It doesn't look like him. His face is flat, like it's been hit with a shovel. His nose is badly bent, and his lips are sewn together. His hair has also been combed to one side, which makes him even less recognisable. I can't recall the last time he combed his black curly locks. I knew he wouldn't look the same because of the impact of the car that hit him, but I didn't think he'd look like this. I don't know what I was expecting. I guess I just thought it would look like a sleeping version of Dad. But the body in the box in front of us looks like a stranger. We all stand next to the coffin not saying anything, with just the sound of Mum and Katy sniffling filling the room. Sean seems to be holding himself together pretty well. Mum puts her arm around us and says, 'He's in a better place now. He's at peace.' I look at Dad's unrecognisable flattened face and think *surely this isn't what peace looks like?*

Back in the present, all those memories are playing like a slideshow in my mind as I drive home from Dad's grave. I wonder if Mum was right. Is he at peace now? I hope he is. He deserves to be, especially after all the shit that happened in his life.

I arrive back at my empty apartment in the city. My girlfriend,

Jen, is at work today, so I've got the place to myself. The TV seems to be staring right at me. The idea of kicking back on the couch and escaping from this story for a while is appealing. Far more appealing than the spare room, where I've been spending my days away from the newsroom, putting pen to paper as I delve into Mum's story. I've been closing the door, cutting out any natural light. And there, in the darkness, with just the glow of my computer screen, I've been trying to bring Mum's story to life, word by word. The darkness cuts out any distractions, leaving just the images that are being projected in my mind. But the images – of Mum back in London, alone with a newborn and now *without* that newborn – are just as dark as the room itself. I grab a beer from the kitchen and go into the room, turning out the light and shutting the door. I take a sip and open my laptop, picking up where I left off.

I'm going through notes from my most recent conversation with Mum. We finished up at the point when she'd just said goodbye to Reynagh and handed her over to her adoptive parents. That was it. Her final farewell. It was seemingly the end of her journey with her firstborn daughter. I genuinely don't know what happens next in Mum's life. All I know is where it eventually leads – to marrying Dad and giving birth to Katy, Sean, and me. Everything in between is comprised of missing puzzle pieces, which I must now extract from Mum, one painful conversation at a time. But my trip to Dad's grave has me thinking: what part does he have to play in Mum's story? Does he even deserve to play a part at all? I don't know. But I need to find out. Who knows what I'll learn about my old man along the way.

As I sit in the darkened room of my apartment, another question pops into my head: what drew Mum and Dad together? It's hard for me to imagine them ever being young and in love. In most of my memories of them together, they are fighting. But, of course, there *was* a time, long before that, when they were in love and everything was right with the world. But the more I think about it, the more I think they didn't just end up together. Perhaps they were bound together, perhaps by the same misfortune. Yes, their lives before meeting were completely different. But they were both victims of the same thing, that horrible thing, where shame outweighs love. Yep, Mum and Dad were both victims of *Irish pride*. And in both my father's and my mother's cases, their painful brush with Irish pride began with the birth of a child.

PAST

CHAPTER FIFTEEN

THE ORPHANED BOY

Belfast, 1947.

H is life started as a screaming child, still covered in the bloody remnants of birth before being plucked away by a midwife. His mother sank back into her hospital bed, panting for breath, red-faced and dripping in sweat. She didn't look at her baby boy as he was carried away. She shut her eyes as tears trickled from them. Her parish priest and social worker had both told her that this would be the last chance she'd get to see her child. But still, she didn't look. She couldn't bring herself to look. The little boy cried like any other child that's just come into the world. He was examined by the doctor and given a clean bill of health. He was then placed in a crib in the nursery with the other newborns. But their fate was far more certain than his.

A small white card was placed on his crib with the name John Patrick Donnelly written on it. It was a name the little boy had no choice in. But it was a name that placed him on one side of a conflict that had its grip around the north of Ireland. To be born with the name Donnelly made it clear to anyone in the country that John was a Catholic. And to be born as a Catholic in the midst of a region divided by religion meant John would forever be branded as a Catholic, as though it was etched in ink on his forehead.

An orphanage in Belfast became his home for the first few years of his life. Other boys who had been given up just like him became his brothers. And there were plenty of them in Belfast in the 1950s. Contraception was unheard of. And religious pride ruled above the laws that any court in the land could impose. Children born out of wedlock were destined to one path. And it was orphanages like John's in Belfast where they ended up.

John was a quiet, shy young boy. He never said much to the other orphans. Perhaps he was scared of talking because the Christian Brothers, who ran the orphanage, yelled at boys whenever they spoke in class. 'Shut yeer trap!' they'd shout, slapping their wooden canes down on the desk. If a Christian Brother was in a particularly bad mood, the cane would be slapped on the boys' hands or heads instead of the desk (the Christian Brothers were in particularly bad moods most of the time). Some of the orphans complained among themselves about the way they were treated by the brothers, or the fact that they had no parents. Not John, though. In his early years, he didn't know any better, so he had no inclination to feel sorry for himself. But when he reached the tender age of five, he was told that he was not a *normal* child. 'You're a bastard, John! We're all bastards!' The blunt declaration came from the mouth of an older child at the orphanage – a boy no older than ten, who had also been brought there as a newborn, fresh from the nursery of the local hospital. That boy's words changed John. All of a sudden, he started to yearn for more. He dreamed of having a mother and father who would rescue him from the orphanage and give him a proper childhood. All children want for something. John's only want was a family of his own.

In his sixth year of life, while crammed into a classroom with dozens of the other orphans, John was asked the question that would change his life forever. 'Shut up, the lotta ye!' Brother O'Sullivan yelled at the young orphans, who instantly went quiet. 'Listen up now. I've got something very important to ask. Who wants to go to ... *Australia*?'

The orphans sat in silence, staring at Brother O'Sullivan through wide eyes.

'What's Oz-trailer?' one of the boys whispered to the boy sitting next to him.

'Shhh,' Brother O'Sullivan hissed. 'No yappering, McDonald! Just hands up if you want to go.'

The silence resumed. All of the boys looked dumbfounded – uncertain whether yes or no was the *correct* answer (getting answers correct was always important to avoid a slap of the cane from the brothers).

'Come on now,' Brother O'Sullivan shouted again. 'Point those hands towards our Lord above if ye want to go!'

Suddenly, one of the boys at the front of the class slowly raised his hand. A moment later, a couple of the boys sitting next to him did the same thing. In a matter of seconds, almost everyone in the class had followed their lead and raised their little hands over their heads. John looked around the room, then out the window at the gloomy grey sky, then back at Brother O'Sullivan. Not wanting to be left out, he thrust his hand into the air. Every boy in the packed classroom was now doing it. And in doing so, they agreed to a new life across the sea – at the bottom of the earth.

Like most of the boys at the orphanage in Belfast, John knew nothing about Australia. He'd spent his early years learning about the 'one, holy, Catholic and apostolic Church.' He learnt about sin and how Jesus died on the cross so sinners like his parents would still be able to get into heaven one day. He'd also learnt about the history of Ireland, and how the British had 'tormented the poor Catholics for eight hundred years'. But the Christian Brothers never taught John or the other orphans anything about Australia. Australia had never even been mentioned in class, or anywhere in the orphanage, until the question was posed by Brother O'Sullivan that day.

At just six years of age, John stood upon the deck of a gigantic ship with hundreds of fellow orphans as they sailed out from Belfast.

'See that yard over there in the harbour?' one of the orphans said to John.

'Aye,' John replied.

'That's where the Irish built the Titanic. Brother Lowry says tis the best ting to ever come out of Ireland ... because it killed fifteen hundred English!'

The boy cracked up. John hoped the ship he was on wasn't built by the same people who built the Titanic or he'd end up at the bottom of the ocean as well. But thankfully he hadn't seen any English people on board just yet, so he figured he'd probably be safe.

Some of the orphans started waving enthusiastically towards the harbour as they drifted further away from it. Some even yelled out, 'Goodbye, Ireland!' Soon enough, all the boys on the ship's deck were laughing and smiling, yelling goodbye, and waving in unison at the land they were leaving. John looked back at the harbour as it became smaller, wondering if his parents would ever come and find him in Australia. The blue skies above the ship abruptly disappeared beneath a mass of dark grey and black clouds. Rain pelted down upon them like great big bullets of stinging water, scattering the orphans like ants as they made for the cabins. In the chaos, John tried to look back towards Ireland one final time. But any glimpse of the land was hidden behind the pack of orphans scrambling for shelter. He thought he'd never see Ireland again.

They spent weeks at sea, bobbing around in the mountainous unforgiving waves at the mercy of whatever the heavens hurled down at them. Many of the young orphans, including John, had never set foot on board a ship before. Their guts churned as the ship rose up over waves as big as buildings then dipped down the back of them. Once one boy started throwing up, others followed, turning the sleeping cabins into a chorus of gagging and retching and soiling them with the sour stench of spew. About a week after they last saw land, the sickness started coming out of other places. The boys would queue outside the bathrooms, squirming in agony, praying they'd make it to the toilet before it fell out their arse ends. If that did happen, the boys would have to clean it up quick smart or they'd have a beating from a brother to look forward to.

Every day, John looked out his tiny round cabin window towards the horizon. He dreamed of what his life would be like in Australia. It would be a proper life. He'd have a mother and father, maybe even brothers and sisters to play with. It would be a life without the nasty Christian Brothers or their slapping canes. Everything would be great in Australia. He knew it. He was convinced his dreams would finally come true when he eventually got to the other side of the world.

John first set foot on Australian soil in the port of Fremantle, just south of Perth, on the west coast of Australia. He and his fellow orphans arrived just like the British convicts had centuries earlier – mustered off a ship like cattle. John marched in line with his suitcase in hand among hundreds of boys as they descended down the rattling metal ramps. The salty smell of the ocean still lingered, but an air of searing heat consumed John as though he was standing in front of a roaring fire. He'd never felt warmth like this before. Half a dozen brothers, dressed in white robes with chunky wooden crucifixes hanging from their necks, were standing in the car park, where wavy lines hovered over the bitumen because of the scorching heat. One of the brothers, with bright red hair and a sun-kissed face, stepped forward and addressed John and the other orphans.

'Welcome, boys!' he said. 'I am Brother Kelly. Yes, you're now down under and closer to the gates of hell itself. But make no mistake, the Lord is as much around these parts as he is in good old Ireland. There is no sin he does not see. He saw what your parents did to bring you into the world. And it hurt our Lord to see such things ... as much as it hurt when the nails went through his hands and feet as he was placed upon the cross. Pontius Pilate may have crucified our Lord, but your parents rubbed salt in his wounds with their wicked behaviour. You are all the spurn of sinners. Don't forget that, boys. The Lord certainly does not. Now ... you see these buses behind me? Each bus is destined for a different place. You will stand and wait in line until the brothers behind me tell you what bus to get on. You don't pick the bus you want to get on. You don't follow your friends onto the bus they get on. You stand on the spot, where you are right now, and you wait for the brothers to tell you what bus to get on. Am I clear on that, boys?'

There was silence. Some boys nodded, but most stood still, most likely overcome by the unfamiliar heat.

'I said, am I *clear* on that, boys?'

'You are, Brother Kelly,' the orphans chorused.

The brothers in white robes walked along the line of orphans, yelling out names.

'Seamus Healy! Bus one!'

'Michael McLaughlin! Bus two!'

'Thomas Doherty! Bus three!'

'Daniel Byrne! Bus four!'

One by one, the orphans were pulled out of line by the brothers and ushered onto the waiting buses. They were sorted through and separated like lambs being sold at a market. John watched on as some boys screamed and cried as they were dragged away from their friends. The brothers were quick to whack those boys over the head to shut them up.

'John Donnelly. Bus two!' one of the brothers finally yelled.

John approached the bus, his feet burning through the soles of his shoes, which had been worn away to barely a slither. He stepped onto the bus, looking back at the trembling boys who were still waiting to be sorted. He'd spent almost every day of his life with some of them. He doubted he'd ever see them again.

When night fell, the temperature did not. John lay above the musky-smelling sheets of his rock-hard bed. Unable to sleep, he stared at the cobwebs on the timber beams on the ceiling. His feet were filthy, still bearing the stains of the brown dirt he'd had to tread over barefooted on his way to the dormitory. He'd been forced to throw his shoes away earlier, along with the other orphans, because they would not be suitable for the Aussie bush.

But they hadn't yet been given new shoes. John could hear the rustling of sheets as other boys stirred in their beds. He assumed they must have also been struggling to sleep in the sweltering heat. One boy, who was two beds over from John, quietly sobbed beneath his sheets. It grew louder as the night went on until eventually the dorm room door swung open and Brother Woods walked in.

'What in the Lord's name is going on in here?' Brother Woods shouted.

None of the boys said a word. Brother Woods walked around the room, trying to find the source of the whimpering. He found the crying boy and ripped the sheets off him. 'What's the matter with ya?' he yelled.

The boy, who was no more than seven years old, continued to sniffle but said nothing. Brother Woods slapped him over the top of the head. The boy yelped like a misbehaving dog being brought into line by its owner.

'What is it, boy? Is your bladder near your eyes?' Brother Woods hit the boy again. 'Are ya a baby, boy? Are ya crying for your mother? She's not coming. Now shut ya trap or I'll put my fist through it.'

The boy continued to whimper, which seemed to enrage Brother Woods further. He raised his hand again and thrust it down upon the boy's face, sending a slapping sound around the room. He grabbed the boy by the arms, yanking him out of bed and dragging him out the door. The boy's crying turned into howling, which could still be heard through the paper-thin walls, even after the door was slammed shut. But the boy's muffled cries gradually faded away, as he was no doubt led to a faraway room where he would be dealt the rest of his punishment. John and the other orphans didn't dare make a sound for the rest of the night.

From the green fields and grey heavens of Ireland to a dusty brown land beneath a cloudless summer sky, Australia was unlike anything John had imagined. The Aussie sun wasn't like the sun in Ireland; it was harsh, with an unrelenting sting in it. And it only took one day to transform John's snow-white skin into a bright shade of cherry red. The heat was also unbearable for him and his fellow orphans. Even the hottest day in Belfast didn't come close to a summer day in Australia. The little Irish boys were always panting, red-faced and dripping in sweat, whether they were sitting in class listening to the drone of the Christian Brothers, or performing manual labour in the dorms and yard, or walking barefoot across the scorching ground. They were perpetually hot and bothered.

Everything around them was foreign to John, from the vast expanses of dusty lifeless ground to the thick sprawling bush with all its prickly glory. There was so much to get used to. Like the humongous brown furry spiders that were twice the size of John's hands. And the much smaller black ones, with a dash of red on their backs, that were apparently very deadly. And the highly venomous brown snakes that lurked under his dorm room building and in the surrounding bush. But unlike some of the boys, those things didn't really worry him much. He'd always had a fascination with animals, and Australia was full of them. He was captivated at the sight of kangaroos as tall as men hopping through the bush, their joeys just behind them. And the wide-eyed possums that crawled around the roof at night. And the majestic pink cockatoos that soared against the bright blue sky.

John found pleasure in Australia through his love of animals, as he did with music. He'd loved music ever since he first heard the rumblings of Irish rebel songs from the other boys at the orphanage in Belfast. Within each song was the passion, the intensity, the uniting anger of a people who felt subjugated in their own land. The Catholic resistance of Northern Ireland used music as their battle cry against the protestants and the British. John was captivated by those songs. They seemed to resonate with him. Not that he really was a victim of the British or the Protestants. They had never done anything to him. No, John was a victim of his own life, of what his own parents had done to him, and then of course the Christian Brothers. But listening to rebel songs in Belfast and now Australia, although strictly forbidden by the brothers, allowed John to deal with some of his anger about his own misfortunes. In Australia, John discovered other, more traditional music. The likes of The Beatles and Elvis Presley were there for John when his parents were not. As were the other child migrants he was growing up with. The young boys were always there for each other – playing games in the bush when they weren't in class or doing their chores, sharing jokes and banter, consoling each other after a beating from the brothers, and singing songs from their homeland. The boys fought at times as well, throwing insults around and sometimes punches and rocks if it got really heated. But fighting aside, all the young boys really were like brothers – a somewhat unfortunate title considering the way they were treated by the Christian Brothers.

The Christian Brothers seemed to be different in Australia. John thought the heat might have done something to them, but he wasn't quite sure. Their tempers seemed shorter – it only took a wrong answer in class or a cough during prayer time, or sometimes nothing at all, to prompt a swift and painful smack over the head with the cane. Boys who talked back were thumped even harder, sometimes with a closed fist, sometimes repeatedly, but always in front of the other young boys so they'd know what happened if they, too, misbehaved. But it was what the brothers did after dark that weighed most heavily on the minds of John and the other orphans.

Every night was the same. A cluttered dorm room lined with creaky timber beds. There were about ten of them, and in each there was a young boy, parentless and afraid. About an hour after bedtime, the door would screech open, spilling blinding white light from the hallway into the pitch-black room. Heavy footsteps followed. *Thud. Thud.* The white robes of a brother could be seen moving through the room, the smell of alcohol on his breath. John kept his eyes shut, pretending he was asleep. But he never was; none of the boys ever were. *Thud. Thud.* The sound of footsteps echoed around the room, rising up from the wooden floorboards. *Thud. Thud.* John held his breath as his heart thumped furiously in his chest. *Thud. Thud.* The steps drew closer. *Thud. Thud.* John's heart was now beating so hard, he could hear it in his ears. *Thud. Thud.* The steps were now right next to him. *Thud. Thud.* The noise cut out, sending the room into an eerie quietness. But only for a moment. The soft rustling of sheets broke the silence. *Thud. Thud.* The footsteps continued, but the sound was now mixed with the soft pitter-patter of a child in tow. The door banged shut behind the footsteps, leaving the dorm room in darkness again.

Some nights, more than one brother arrived in the darkness. It was usually a different child who was taken each night. But there were the favourites – the boys who were pulled out of bed and led away more often than not. As for what happened to the boys who were chosen, none ever spoke of it. But John knew what happened. He knew the brothers made the boys do dirty things, shameful things, but above all, *secret* things. He always kept his eyes scrunched shut during the nightly ordeal when the brothers roamed, as he clasped onto his dream of a life with a family of his own. He still hadn't let go of that dream. He imagined how his parents would storm into the room and save John before the brother could get to him. But every night as that figure in the darkness came to take one of the children, John felt his dream slipping further away. He realised that his parents were never coming to save him, or any of the other children for that matter. All he could do was hide under his covers, pretending to sleep, and hope the wandering brother would not choose him to be taken away in the night.

After more than a decade in Australia, John's dream of being rescued by his family had faded away, almost to nothingness. He was a boy on the cusp of manhood. And while he wasn't yet legally an adult, John had already developed an attitude that is inherently part of adulthood – an acceptance of life as it is, with all its pain and misery, and a reluctance to dream of a better life. John knew what he was. And that would never change. He was a bastard, discarded by his parents, abandoned in an orphanage, and shipped off to the bottom of the earth. He carried that realisation with him into adulthood. He had grown into a young man who was sometimes shy, sometimes charismatic, a lover of wild animals and music, and a doggedly loyal mate to the boys he'd grown up with. And while his Irish roots remained entrenched within him, on the surface he was now an Aussie, thanks to his sun-tinged skin and ocker twang. But beyond all the things John seemed to be, there was no changing that he'd become a broken young man, resigned to the fact his parents were never coming to save him.

It wasn't until John turned twenty-one that he again set his heart on meeting his mother and father. The re-emergence of his dream was prompted by the words of a priest in Perth.

'We've found them, John,' the priest told him. 'Your mother

and father. They're married now. Living in Northern Ireland still. Just outside Belfast. You can go there to meet them if you want?'

He had wanted to hear those words for most of his childhood. But now that they were actually being muttered, the true enormity of what it meant finally dawned on him. He could very soon come face-to-face with the man and woman who abandoned him. The same man and woman who let him suffer at the hands of the Christian Brothers in Belfast and Australia. His body seized up whenever he thought of his parents. He questioned whether he would break down in tears and wrap his arms around them when they finally came face-to-face, or whether he would turn his back on his mother and throw his fist at his father. He didn't know how he'd feel or what he'd do when he finally met them. The only way to find out was to return to his homeland.

John arrived back in Belfast as a twenty-two-year-old, this time travelling on a plane instead of a sickness-inducing lumbering ship. A nun who worked at John's former orphanage in Belfast had got in touch with John's parents to inform them of his imminent return.

'Oh aye,' John's mother said to the nun over the phone. ''Twould be a sin to deny the request of a nun like yourself. I'll meet the boy. But it can't be here at me home. I'm sure ye understand. The neighbours ... you see ... they would be peeking ... and start asking questions. There would be talk. And *talk* would be good for no one, the boy included.'

'Your son is comin' all the way from Australia to see you!' the nun barked back at Mrs Donnelly. 'The least you can do is bring him into your home.'

Mrs Donnelly didn't dare argue with the nun. And so John arrived in Belfast and was taken by two nuns to County Tyrone, where he would finally meet his parents for the first time. He and the nuns stood in the cold in front of the little white cottage, their breaths turning to mist in front of their faces, just like John remembered as a child. The front door swung open. John's mother stood in the doorway. She was wearing a long black dress with streaks of grey through her dark hair and green eyes just like John's.

'Hello,' Mrs Donnelly said, looking at the two nuns but not at John. 'Come in then.'

John and the nuns sat at the kitchen table as Mrs Donnelly prepared tea.

'Where's your husband?' the older of the two nuns asked.

'At the pub,' Mrs Donnelly said, sighing.

'At the pub?' the old nun replied, raising her eyebrows. 'What sort of man sees filling his gut with pints as more important than meeting his firstborn?'

Mrs Donnelly didn't answer as she poured tea for John and the two nuns.

'Where are your others?' the old nun asked Mrs Donnelly.

Mrs Donnelly's face seemed to tighten. She hesitated for a moment.

'I'll bring them in,' she said.

Mrs Donnelly returned to the kitchen a few minutes later. Three boys and two girls, all in their teens, followed behind. The children gathered around the table on the opposite side of John. They were wide-eyed and appeared to have no idea as to why they had been summoned into their kitchen. John's hands and legs trembled, and his eyes darted around the room. He felt out of place, just as he had when he first arrived in Australia all those years earlier. The old nun broke the silence.

'Listen in, children. You would be wondering who this young

man is and what he's doing here in your kitchen. You would be right to wonder. I'm here to tell you. This is John ... he's your brother.'

The mouths of the three boys and two girls fell open.

The old nun continued talking, unfazed by their reaction. 'Your mother gave birth to John before she had all of you. And before she was married to your father. And we know how the Lord looks on these things. Good Irish women, like you girls will grow into one day, must only bear children after they have married. But your parents have asked the Lord's forgiveness for their sins. And we know that the Lord is forgiving to those who truly repent. And that means ... we all need to forgive your parents as well.'

Mrs Donnelly was standing at the sink, staring out the window, away from her children and the nuns.

The old nun continued talking. 'Your brother. John here was raised by the Christian Brothers in Australia. He's here because he wants to meet you. All of you. 'Twould have been a great sin to deny him that. Now ... I'm sure there are things you want to say, or questions you want to ask. Now is the time to speak.'

The Donnelly children, whose shock was still apparent by their open mouths, said nothing.

'Lord above,' the old nun said. 'The lotta you look like you've seen the ghost of Saint Patrick himself! Is there nothing you want to say to John ... your own brother?'

Unpleasant silence filled the room again. John felt about as unwelcome and unloved as he ever had. He couldn't bring himself to look at his siblings or his mother. He just stared down at his feet, thinking the silence would never end. But then, it suddenly did. It was cut short by the screeching of a chair as it was abruptly pulled out from the kitchen table. John looked up and saw a black-haired girl, no older than fifteen, marching around the table towards him. She crouched down and wrapped her arms around him, squeezing him tightly, warmly. John felt his jaw quivering while his sight became blurry. He had never been gripped in a hug as tight as this. In fact, he couldn't recall the last time he'd been hugged.

'My brother,' the black-haired girl whispered as tears trickled down her cheeks. 'You're finally home.'

CHAPTER SIXTEEN

EIGHTEEN YEARS

Reynagh's First Birthday

An entire year had passed since Reynagh took her first gasps of life in Epping Hospital. During those twelve months, she would have started to crawl and probably taken her first stumbling steps. Her voice would have developed as the days passed, starting out as the incoherent ramblings of an infant before eventually muttering her first distinct words. Was her first word *Mum*? Perhaps it was *Dad*. Her mother and father, brothers and sisters would have become familiar to her during those first twelve months. The mere sight of them was probably enough to bring a smile to her little face. She probably smiled a lot as she became more aware of the world around her. And what a beautiful world it would have been. Her loving family would have made sure of that.

While Debra and Rob and their children would have been celebrating Reynagh's first birthday, Bridget was in the midst of her new life. She had left London, where there were too many reminders of Reynagh and the pain of her loss. She was now working as a nurse at a hospital in Essex (not far from the mother and baby home in Epping, in fact). She had moved there hoping a change of scenery would help her heal. But it hadn't. There was no escaping what had happened in the past year. She was reminded of Reynagh every day. It was triggered by the sight of a mother and her child on the street, or a newborn in the hospital, or a family in a shop. Whatever the trigger was, Bridget always felt the same – as though a knife was slowly plunging into her chest. She thought the searing pain that came with every reminder of Reynagh was part of her penance. She believed it was the cross she had to bear, the guilt she deserved to suffer. So she never let it show. Even if the sensation struck her mid-sentence, even if it hit while she was attending to a patient, even if she was in the middle of joking around with her colleagues at the hospital. She *never* let the pain out. It stayed where she thought it belonged: inside. She simply carried on and carried the pain within. And every day as she woke and worked and slept, there were recurring words that rang in her ears. Words that she'd heard many times during her stay at the mother and baby home. But now they were the words that kept her going. *It's for the best.*

On Reynagh's first birthday, Bridget woke at 6 a.m. and got ready for her shift in the hospital. It was a day like any other. She did her morning rounds, cheerfully greeting patients from room to room. 'Good morning, Mr Jasper, how was your sleep? Oh, that's grand … How are you feeling today, Mr Smith? Time for your bath, Mrs Wallis … Don't ye be spitting that food on the floor, Mrs Walters.' Her patients were usually a welcome distraction from her troubles. But today they were not truly on her mind. All she could think of was her little girl. *Is she awake yet? What presents is she getting? Are her brothers and sisters keeping her company? How much has she grown? Is she healthy? Is she happy?*

The questions nagged away in her head as she gave bed baths and meds, wrapped bandages, and dressed wounds – in between listening to the ramblings of her patients. The questions didn't relent as the day went on, and neither did that familiar stabbing pain in her chest. A year earlier, she had been holding Reynagh in her arms at Epping Hospital. She had been completely exhausted after the gruelling hours of labour. Her fears had given way to an unexpected contentment as she held her baby during those first precious moments of bonding. Reynagh was a part of her life back then, so she wasn't yet familiar with the emptiness that would take hold of it. But now, a year on, there was no way of getting to her little girl. There was no way of wishing her a happy birthday or giving her a kiss and a hug. All Bridget could do was carry on with her day and keep her little girl in her thoughts, despite the stabbing pain that came with them.

She lay in bed after her shift as midnight approached. She was restless; every little movement sent creaks around the room. The day was rapidly slipping away, and so too was Reynagh's first birthday. It would be the first of many that Bridget would be absent from. She wondered if the next one would hurt as much as this. *Please, Lord,* she prayed as she tossed and turned in bed. *Keep Reynagh safe. Bring her health and happiness. Watch over her and her family. And, Lord ... please forgive me for what I've done.*

Reynagh's Second Birthday
Perth, Australia, 1973

They had never been this far apart. As Reynagh's family was celebrating her second birthday in Nottingham, Bridget was a world away in Australia. All of mainland Europe, Africa, and Asia, and the surrounding seas and oceans lay between them. While another year had passed, Bridget's pain had not. It lingered, incurably, as she suspected it always would.

Bridget had travelled to Perth, a small city on the west coast of Australia, several months earlier for her brother Tony's wedding. Tony had made a life for himself in Australia, finding work and now a wife. They had even asked Bridget to be a bridesmaid at the wedding. A flood of scorching hot air crashed into her as she stepped off the plane, while a swarm of flies droned around her face. Tony, six feet six, with curly bright red hair and gangly limbs, waved enthusiastically at the sight of her, as did his soon-to-be wife, Paula, who was standing alongside him. Bridget's sister, Maureen, who had moved to Australia years earlier to become a nun, was also there to greet her. Maureen wept with joy and wrapped her arms around Bridget – their first embrace in many long years.

Despite the heat, which was so foreign to Bridget, she instantly felt at home in Australia. Even though it was classified as a city, Perth was more like a really big town. The downtown area of the 'city' itself was made up of less than a dozen biggish buildings (most of which could hardly be classified as high-rise) along the sprawling Swan River. The river split Perth into two parts – the north and south, with suburbs on either side stretching no further than a thirty-minute drive. And driving was necessary to get anywhere in Perth. There was no underground train system, and getting anywhere by bus required patience and spare time. Bridget was surprised to see so many stars in the sky on her first night in town. Unlike London and every other city she'd been to, Perth wasn't covered in a blanket of night-time haze that blocked out the glowing expanses of the universe. It was a welcome and familiar sight for an Irish girl, who was the farthest from home she'd ever been.

She considered staying in Perth after Tony's wedding. But it wasn't an easy decision to make. She figured Australia was a long way away from the whispers of gossip in Belmullet, making it hard for her shame to follow her here. But it was also a long way away from her little girl. Not that she was *hers* any more. And not that living on the other side of the world would make a difference. It wouldn't matter if Bridget lived in Australia, or London, or Belmullet, or Epping, or Nottingham, or anywhere on the planet. It wasn't simply distance that was keeping them apart. So what would it matter if Bridget settled in Australia? She was forbidden from seeing Reynagh, and that would never change. That was her reasoning in making the decision to stay. It would be her chance to make a fresh start in a foreign land, where she'd have her brother and sister to keep her company.

It didn't take Bridget long to find work after the wedding. She took a nursing job at a local private hospital, St John of God. And she was rapidly making friends, just as she had when she first moved to London as an eighteen-year-old (sadly she had barely spoken to her friends from London since she'd left). It turned out Perth was full of twenty-something-year-old Irish expats, who'd been lured down under by the long warm days, pristine beaches, and well-paying jobs. Bridget never told any of her new friends about Reynagh. In fact, she hadn't spoken to *anyone* about Reynagh since she'd last laid eyes on her. She still believed it was solely her burden to carry. She had no intention of confiding in anyone about it, including her own family.

When the fifteenth of July, Reynagh's second birthday, came around, Bridget felt just as rotten as she had a year earlier. She had the day off work and was catching up with Maureen at her flat in a beachside suburb.

'What is it?' Maureen asked, her eyes narrowed. 'What's wrong?'

Bridget sipped her tea, trying to mask her sorrow. 'I'm fine,' she said.

Maureen's glare didn't relent. 'There *is* something wrong. What is it? Tell me!'

Bridget took another sip of her tea as nonchalantly as she could manage. 'I had a child,' she blurted out. She suddenly froze, her face instantly burning as it underwent its regular red transformation. She couldn't believe those words had just come from her mouth, words she hadn't muttered in years.

Maureen's mouth was wide open, as were her eyes. She was dead still. 'You what?' she said finally.

'I'm sorry,' Bridget said, before burying her face into her hands, her palms filling with tears. Then she felt a hand upon her back and a head against her shoulder.

'It's okay,' Maureen whispered in her ear. 'You don't need to be sorry. It's okay.'

They released their embrace and stared into each other's eyes.

'What about Mammy and Daddy?' Maureen asked.

'They know,' Bridget said softly.

'And? What have they done to help you?'

Bridget didn't respond, thinking it would be better if she didn't speak ill of her parents.

'What did they say?' Maureen persisted.

'Nothing,' Bridget said.

'Nothing!' Maureen snarled. 'Their youngest daughter has a child and they've got *nothing* to say?'

'Well ... they had plans.'

'What plans?' Maureen said, her voice rising.

Bridget instantly regretted bringing this up. She considered keeping her mouth shut and not saying another word. But Maureen was still glaring at her, waiting for an answer.

'They wanted Aunty Ellen to take the baby,' Bridget said. 'They were going to pretend it was hers.'

'Ellen!' Maureen gasped in a high-pitched voice. 'You can't be serious. That's ... bloody awful, Bridget.'

Maureen sat for a moment, staring blankly at the floor. It looked like she was muttering something to herself under her breath. 'How can they treat you like this?'

Bridget didn't answer. She felt like she didn't have the right to answer.

'When did you have the child?'

'Two years ago,' Bridget said. 'Her name's Reynagh. I wish you could have seen her, Maureen. She was so ... perfect.'

'Where'd you have her?'

'Just outside London. In a place called Epping. That's where I was sent. So no one would see me. It was a place for unmarried mothers, you see.'

Maureen's lower lip quivered. 'The bastards!' she hissed through gritted teeth. 'Forgive my language, Lord. But ... the bloody bastards! How could they do this to you, Bridget? How could they leave you all alone?'

'Some of my friends from London were great,' Bridget said.

Maureen burst into tears. 'Lord above,' she said, rubbing her eyes. '*Friends* ... what about the rest of us?'

'I'm sorry, Maureen,' Bridget said. 'I hope the Lord can forgive me.'

'Of course he forgives you,' Maureen said. 'But what about the way you were treated? *They* are the ones who need to ask for forgiveness.'

'It's alright,' Bridget said.

'No, it's not. You needed support. Not to be sent away all by yourself.'

Bridget placed her hand upon Maureen's, which was resting on the table.

'I'm glad I'm here with you now,' Bridget said.

'You can never give anyone the satisfaction,' Maureen said. 'The satisfaction of grovelling to them for forgiveness. Because that's what they'll want ... for you to beg for forgiveness. But you just hold your head high, Bridget. Don't let them look down on ya. By Lord, anyone that does should be feckin' asking the Lord for forgiveness themselves!'

First Day of High School

More than ten years had passed since Bridget had last laid eyes on Reynagh. In a way, it was inconceivable that they'd been apart for so long. But in another way, life went on. Just as Bridget had been told it would. Reynagh was growing up, not before her eyes, but a world away. And Bridget's life simply carried on. As did the guilt, the shame, the hurt. At times, it subsided, but it always lingered – it was still that incurable illness. She simply learnt to live with it, as it stirred away within.

Bridget did all the things that any Irish woman in her twenties does while living abroad. She made friends and travelled, nursing at whatever hospital would give her work. She crammed into pubs and clubs on Saturday nights, singing and dancing into the wee hours, spending the little money she had. She lived in dilapidated flats with other young nurses, most of whom were also from Ireland. She watched the sun set over the Indian Ocean as it cast golden light over the jagged west coast. She traversed the vast brown desert to the other side of Australia, where she dug her toes into the white sand of Bondi Beach along with other tourists whose skin was also red and white, like candy canes. She drove a little rusted car that backfired and only started when it felt like it. She watched in awe as kangaroos hopped through the bush and jumped in terror at the rustling sound of snakes. After the misery of saying goodbye to Reynagh a decade earlier, Bridget had managed to salvage the rest of her twenties. But among the excitement of her adventures in Australia, she never truly felt complete. It was as though she'd somehow lost an internal organ but couldn't pinpoint what it was. Her heart was still beating, her lungs still drawing breath, everything seemed to be working as it should. But there was *something* missing. She knew it. She could feel it. Or rather, she could feel its absence. But no doctor would have been able to diagnose it. It was a condition that only other unmarried mothers, who were separated from their babies, would have been able to understand – a classic case of Inexplicable Incompleteness.

She still thought about Reynagh every day. And whenever she saw a girl who was a similar age to Reynagh, a barrage of questions flooded her head. *How big is she now? How is she doing in school? What does she want to be when she grows up? Does she ever think of me? Is she healthy? Is she happy?* Bridget knew it was pointless to ask herself these questions. They may well have lived on different planets, because there was no way they could get to each other. They were separated by oceans, but they were kept apart by law. *Hope* was now the only thing that kept her going. The hope that one day they'd be together again.

When Reynagh was starting high school in England, Bridget was living back in Perth, where her Australian journey had started. The lasting image of Reynagh, which was burned onto her retinas, was of a small child, not yet a toddler. A cute little girl with thick black locks and striking brown eyes. It was hard to comprehend that she was now a high school kid, treading the emotional minefield of female adolescence. She was also edging closer to adulthood in the eyes of the law. She'd soon be given the choice to track down her biological mother. All Bridget could do was wait.

It was a Saturday night, the first since Reynagh would have started high school in England. Bridget had just finished a gruelling twelve-hour shift at the hospital. She was meeting up with her Aussie friend Val, before heading to a pub for a bit of craic.

'There's some lads I want you to meet,' Val said as they drove to the pub. 'They're a bloody laugh! They were actually the little kids who were shipped over here from the orphanages in Ireland all those years ago. But they're great guys. Good fun. You'll like 'em, Bridget.'

'Oh great,' Bridget said, not thinking much of it.

'I've actually had me eye on one of them for a while,' Val said, grinning. 'His name's John. Wouldn't mind if he had a crack at me. But I reckon he's not keen. Wants an Irish girl apparently. *You'd* like him, Bridget.'

Val playfully nudged Bridget, giving her a wink.

They arrived at the pub and met up with the boys, who were cheerfully drinking at the bar. Their names were John, Patrick, and Brendan. They were all of Irish descent, and all in their early thirties, just like Bridget and Val. The five of them enjoyed a chat, a laugh, and a few drinks (which in Bridget's case was lemonade). And then they went their separate ways. Bridget didn't give them another thought. Not until they crossed paths again a few weeks later. This time the lads were at the Irish Club – a regular hangout for Perth's Irish expats. There, the conversation and the laughs continued where it'd left off. Bridget saw John, Patrick, and Brendan during nights out a dozen or so times over the following few months. Their encounters were always the same – a polite hello, a bit of chitchat, a joke or two, and then a casual goodbye. She was always meeting new people and making new friends, practically since she'd left Belmullet as an eighteen-year-old. So, there was nothing really significant about meeting these lads. That is, until she received a phone call out of the blue one night after work.

'Hello,' Bridget answered.

'Ah ... hi ...' A man's voice came through the phone. 'Bridget?'

'Yes,' she said. 'I'm sorry. Who's this?'

'It's John. John Donnelly.'

'Oh ... *John*.' It took her a moment to put a face to the name. 'How are ya?'

'Yeah, good, thanks. I was actually just ringing... umm ... just wondering really if you'd like to ... I dunno ... maybe catch up again some time?'

'Of course,' Bridget replied casually. 'That'd be grand. Tell me, when are you and the boys heading out again?'

'Oh, no, I mean ... umm ... just the *two* of us... If you want, that is.'

'Oh,' Bridget said, her cheeks starting to simmer. 'Well. Yes, of course. The two of us. That'd be grand. Sounds lovely, John.'

Bridget had considered John to be a nice young man during

their previous encounters, but she had never looked at him as anything more than a new friend – in fact, he was probably still a friendly acquaintance more than anything. It's not that she didn't think he was attractive or anything; there was just no initial spark. She actually thought he was quite handsome. He had thick curly black hair, a common heirloom of his native County Tyrone in Northern Ireland. His eyes were a murky shade of green. His skin bore the marks of the Australian sun, sprinkled with freckles and patches of red. And now that she thought of it, he had a nice smile as well – a real genuine sort of smile that created a cluster of wrinkles around his eyes. But Bridget didn't know a great deal about him. She knew he was an Irishman. Not that you'd know it from hearing his voice, which was tinged with an Aussie ocker twang. She knew he was an orphan and had been shipped to Perth as a child. And she knew he had a nice singing voice. She'd even heard it one time, when he took to the stage at an open mic night at the Irish Club. He was a regular apparently, singing the songs of his homeland, like 'Danny Boy', 'Fields of Athenry', and 'Whiskey in the Jar'. But apart from his love of music and his title as an orphan, she knew nothing else about him. He had never said much around her during their brief encounters, in between the frequent sideways glances he shot in her direction. Those little glances made a bit more sense now that he'd asked her out.

A week after the phone call, John picked Bridget up from her flat near the St John of God Hospital, where she still worked.

'You look nice,' he said, opening the door for her. He seemed really nervous – his head was tilted forward as though he was trying to tuck it into his chest. He was fidgeting too, moving his hands from his sides, to his pockets, back to his sides, then clasping them together like a priest in a sermon, before repeating the process all over again. He barely said a word as he drove her to the restaurant. The only noises he was making were little grunts when he cleared his throat. Bridget, whose face was under attack from those familiar burning flushes, did all the talking during the journey. The once shy and quiet girl had transformed into something of a talker over the past decade. Her acquired skill – to talk, even when feeling shy – had probably come about after years of talking to patients and meeting new people on her travels. But still, it wasn't always easy for her, especially in this car ride with John, in which she was single-handedly talking for two.

They went to a small, dimly lit restaurant in the city, which was owned by an old Irish couple (Perth's Irish expats were always supporting their own). And there the conversation picked up a little, prompted by Bridget asking John all sorts of questions about himself. Eventually, as the mains were being served, she asked a question that she'd promised herself she'd avoid all night. Maybe it was because John seemed a bit more relaxed than he did earlier (possibly thanks to few quickly drunk beers during the entre). Or maybe it was because she just couldn't help her curiosity. Whatever it was, the question seemed to slip from her tongue before she had the chance to stop it. Regret set in immediately.

'Can you tell me about your family?' she said, her eyes suddenly widening as she realised what she'd done.

John took a moment to answer. 'They're all in Tyrone,' he said, poking his steak with his fork, like a child does when playing with their food.

'Oh, lovely,' Bridget said. 'You've been back there?'

'Yep,' he said, sipping his beer. 'A few years back.'

He twirled his glass around on the table, not taking his eyes off it and certainly not looking at Bridget. He picked up the glass again and gulped the foamy remnants at the bottom.

'Why'd you leave Ireland?' he asked, looking her in the eye again.

'I wanted to see the world,' she said. 'My brother and sister are here. I came for his wedding. Loved it. And I haven't left since.'

'Well, there's plenty of Paddies in Perth, that's for sure.'

John signalled to the waiter with curled fingers and a flick of the wrist in a drinking motion. Within minutes, he had a full glass of beer in front of him.

Bridget didn't ask him anything about his family for the rest of the dinner, fearing it might strike a nerve. She still did most of the talking, telling him all about her travels around Australia and the people she'd met along the way. John was wearing a toothy grin as he listened. Occasionally he'd quickly look away at something else in the room, as though fearing he'd been caught staring at her too intently.

The date ended where it started, outside Bridget's flat. John gave her a peck on the cheek and wished her a good night. And that was it. The evening was over. But it was also the start of something. They went out again for dinner a few weeks later. Then again, a week after that. She wasn't sure if she wanted a boyfriend. And she wasn't quite sure how she felt about John. But she enjoyed being around him, even when he wasn't saying much. Maybe it was because of the way he looked at her, or maybe it was because of the tingles she felt on the back of her neck when he smiled. She decided to keep seeing him.

The shyness that had struck John during their first few meetings faded away with every date. He was speaking more every time they hung out, revealing glimpses of his younger years, and his love of traditional Irish music and the wild animals of the Aussie bush. He also revealed his charismatic and playful sides. He would often impersonate Bridget's accent, making fun of the way she pronounced words like film (*fillem*), thriller (*triller*), specifically (*pacifically*), and sandwich (*sangwich*). He was constantly making her laugh.

It wasn't love at first sight for Bridget. She fell for John, gradually, gently, more and more with every encounter. From that seemingly innocuous first meeting at a pub, several months later Bridget was in love. It felt the same as it had all those years ago in London. But things were different now. She wasn't a naïve girl any more. She was a woman, and a mother. But not just a regular mother - she was an unmarried mother. It was a title she'd kept relatively hidden for the past decade. But as she got closer with John, she felt a growing urge to tell him the truth about her past.

'There's something you need to know,' Bridget said one Friday night over dinner.

John's green eyes narrowed, clouded with concern. 'What is it?' he asked.

She'd been planning this speech for weeks. But now her carefully planned words abandoned her at the very moment she needed them, like a lead actress forgetting her lines under the bright lights of opening night. She'd wanted to break this news delicately. She'd planned it that way. But as John looked at her through his uncertain eyes as he waited for her answer, delicate seemed impossible. So, she simply spat out, 'I had a child.' She scrunched her eyes shut, fearing the shame upon his face.

'It was a long time ago,' she continued. 'In London. A little girl ... her name's Reynagh. But ... I had to give her up.'

She opened her eyes, expecting to see John looking upon her with disgust. She always braced for judgement when she confided in someone for the first time. But John was not looking at her with judging eyes. He was grinning. And then he chuckled.

'It's alright,' he said, smirking. 'If I were a woman, I'm sure I would have had a dozen kids by now.'

He laughed some more.

'Oh,' Bridget said, a little deflated. 'I was a bit worried you were going to say something different.'

'I could tell,' John said. 'That look on your face ... you looked bloody terrified. It's okay, darling. These things happen when you're young.'

John's response was the exact opposite of what Bridget had been expecting. Especially given his childhood. He had been born out of wedlock, given away at birth, and sent to an orphanage run by nasty men, before being shipped off to the other side of the world where there were even nastier men to deal with. Bridget thought he'd at least feel *something* when she told him that she too had been forced to give a child away.

John's childhood was something he didn't often speak about. Even after six months of dating, he had barely mentioned it. When he did, it had taken whiskey and beer to draw the words from him. And only after drinking more than a casual few would he start to divulge his innermost thoughts and feelings of his troubled past.

'My bitch mother!' he grumbled one night as he scrunched his can of beer and threw it in the bin. 'Do you want to know what she did to me when I went back to see her for the first time? She hides me. Fuckin' *hides* me. After I'd flown around the bloody world to see her. And she hides me in a bedroom when the neighbours come to visit. "Just stay in there while they're here for tea," she says to me. "They can't be seeing ya. It'll be a bad look for the family. I'll knock on the door when ye can come out." Can you believe that? The old bitch! I couldn't care less if she dropped dead tomorrow.'

'Oh,' Bridget muttered, placing a hand on his knee. 'I'm so sorry you had to go through that.'

'And my father ...' John said, opening a fresh can and sending beer foam spraying out, before taking a solid gulp. 'If she's a bitch, then he's ... well he's fuckin' worse. The spineless prick couldn't even face me when I went back there. He ran off to the pub and hid there for days. Barely saw him during my time in town. And when I did ... couldn't look me in the eye ... could barely say two words to me. Gutless piece of shit. I didn't shed a tear the day he died, I can tell ya that. I had a drink, though. To celebrate.'

He gulped another sip of beer, slurping loudly. Bridget took her hand from his knee and leaned away as his voice grew louder.

'I went back to Ireland again after he died,' he said, the bitter smell of beer floating on his breath. 'My mother made me go to his grave. I should have said no. But I didn't. So we went. The whole family. And we stood there in the cemetery, my brothers and sisters praying, my mother crying. And all I wanted to do ... was spit on his fuckin' grave.'

He continued sipping his beer, his nostrils flaring, purple veins popping in his temple. It was a far different John to the man she'd met months earlier, and the man she'd slowly fallen in love with. *Is this what the pain of an abandoned child looks like?* She wondered if Reynagh would hate her, just like John hated his parents. But she also feared she'd never get the chance to find out.

Reynagh's Eighteenth Birthday

The day had come, and Bridget could hardly believe it. Reynagh was now a woman – in the legal sense, that is. This was the day she had been waiting for since their final goodbye in Nottingham all those years ago. So much had changed in Bridget's life since that farewell. She could only imagine what had transpired for Reynagh. Like every year, when the fifteenth of July came around, she spent Reynagh's birthday pondering. *What is she doing now? What presents did she get? Does she have lots of friends? Does she have a boyfriend? How are her family treating her? Does she ever think of me? Is she healthy? Is she happy?* But this birthday was different. For there was another question Bridget kept asking herself over and over again. And now it was a question that could finally be answered.

Does she want to see me?

CHAPTER SEVENTEEN

ALL GROWN UP

Perth, 1984.

'**P**ush,' the doctor yelled.

Bridget did as she was told, pushing with all the remaining strength she had. Her body was half numb from the epidural, while the other half felt like it had been bashed and beaten, inside and out. But with that final push it was finally over. Relief swept across her body as breath returned to her lungs. John was right next to her, clenching her hand so hard his knuckles had turned white. His green eyes were glassy as he looked down at the doctor at the end of the bed, a baby in his arms. Maureen rose from her chair, where she had earlier been banished by one of the nurses for repeatedly yelling 'Push, Bridget!' too loudly. There was a brief stillness in the room as the doctor cut the umbilical cord and examined the newborn. Then the child's mouth opened, releasing a high-pitched squeal – that unmistakably beautiful sound of new life. The doctor then addressed Bridget and John above the screams of their child.

'It's a girl,' he said.

A girl. Bridget couldn't believe it. She had been expecting a boy. She was so convinced, she'd almost painted their nursery blue. A nurse wiped the baby clean with a towel, wrapped her in a small blanket, and handed her over to Bridget. The little girl's cries had now died down. She was so still in her mother's arms. John, who was sniffling, reached out his hand and delicately brushed his daughter's cheek with his calloused fingers. He leaned down and kissed her on the forehead. John and Bridget then cast their eyes away from their little girl and towards each other, smiling and entwining their hands together. Bridget cherished the moment – with their little girl nestled between their bodies. Hers was a life they had *both* created, and they were *both* there in that moment to treasure it, to share it, just as it should have been.

Bridget and John had got engaged two years earlier. They had been sitting at the beach, eating fish and chips and watching the sunset, when the topic of marriage came up.

'Have you thought about when we should get married?' Bridget had asked, casually.

John smirked and scratched his cheek, as he often did when put on the spot with difficult questions. 'Are *you* proposing to me?' he said, still smirking.

'Oh, Lord, no,' Bridget said, taking a bite of her fish. 'Just saying. Just asking, if you've *thought* about it. That's all.'

'Well,' John said, scratching his cheek again, which had turned red. 'I was thinking of buying you a ring and giving it to you on your birthday. But now you know that ... why bother waiting, hey?'

And that was it. No clichés. No grand romantic gestures. It was simply an agreement between the two of them that they wanted to commit to each other through the sacrament of marriage. They even went to the jewellers together to pick the ring. Six months later, they were married. The wedding was a perfect Perth spring day – not a cloud in the sky, with a light ocean breeze making the heat bearable. Bridget's mammy and daddy made the long trip from Belmullet to be there. Even John's brother and sister travelled over from Northern Ireland and were part of the bridal party. After the traditional service in a church, they had a reception ceremony in a thriving garden near the beach. There was plenty of laughter and music as they celebrated. It was a wonderful day.

After their wedding day, they started building a house. It was a simple little weatherboard home with three bedrooms and a bathroom. Nothing fancy. They'd bought ten acres of farming land near a town called Wooroloo, which was about an hour outside of Perth. Their land was covered in golden-brown high grass, the fields sloping down towards a thick line of sprawling trees and a trickling creek. And it was all surrounded by the ragged Australian bush. They soon had a beautiful golden retriever named Sandy. Then came the chickens, the sheep, the goat, the birds, and all the wild animals that John was always rescuing. He'd regularly return from his travels in the bush with a new member of their little family. Like the injured baby bird who'd fallen from a treetop nest, and the orphaned joey he'd saved from the pouch of its dead mother on the roadside. Their little farm was the perfect place to nourish their love of animals. But it was also the perfect place to raise a family. Soon enough after their wedding, Bridget fell pregnant (not for the first time, of course). And while the feeling of a child growing inside her was familiar, it was so very different this time. She felt no need to hide what was happening to her. She didn't have to take refuge in her room, only to conceal her bulging belly with loose clothing whenever she ventured outside of it. She didn't have to go into work early so she could throw up in the empty bathroom without drawing attention to herself. She wouldn't be sent off to some hidden institution where she'd work her fingers to the bone and cry herself to sleep at night. This time, she felt as though she was allowed to embrace what was happening to her. It was okay to glow and gloat in public, like all other pregnant women do. She was allowed to call her mother and tell her the wonderful news.

'I'm pregnant, Mammy,' she said over the phone one evening.

'Brilliant,' her mother's voice came down the line. 'Thank the Lord. I must tell your father at once. Hold on. Michael! Michael! Michael! Jesus, Mary, and Joseph, he's gone deaf in his old age. Michael! It's Bridget on the phone. Your daughter ... In Australia! Guess what? She's having a baby!'

There wasn't as much uncertainty this time either. Bridget was aware of the pain that was awaiting her in the labour, as though it was stitched into the fibres of her muscle memory. When the labour did come, it bloody hurt, just as she remembered it hurting all those years ago in Epping. But at least she wasn't alone this time. John was by her side, clenching her hand, telling her, 'It's alright ... keep going ... you're doing great ... almost there.'

And then, after the birth, that magical moment came when Bridget held her little girl, John standing at her bedside, both of them glowing, both elated beyond words as they admired the life they had created. Maureen was also weeping with joy.

'What's her name then?' she asked.

'Katy,' Bridget answered. 'That was the name we picked out for a girl.'

'It's after my sister,' John said, smiling proudly. John's sister Katy had been the first of his siblings to embrace him all those years ago when he'd first gone back to Ireland. She'd been his favourite ever since.

Bridget and John started raising their little girl on their farm in Wooroloo. They shared the moments she took her first clumsy steps, and then when she spoke her first words, which were 'Mum' and 'Dad'. Bridget often felt intoxicated with joy as she watched Katy grow. But there was also the constant state of sleep deprivation to deal with. She was summoned out of bed by Katy's cries several times a night. There was no time to rest during the day, in between the regular feeding and nappy changes, and the perpetual cleaning that was required around the house. But the lack of sleep didn't bother Bridget. She was doing what she felt she'd always been destined to do. She cherished her one-on-one time with Katy during the day, before sharing precious family time with John at night. Their little weatherboard home was constantly filled with the sounds of laughter and lullabies, in between the soft mutterings and screeching yells of an infant. To Bridget, they were the sounds of a perfectly happy little family. And while the idea of peace and quiet was sometimes appealing, especially during the sleepless nights, she never wanted those sounds to stop.

Less than two years after Katy was born, Bridget fell pregnant again. This time, she and John welcomed a little boy into the world. They named him Sean – another Irish name, of course. Again, the pain of childbirth was quickly conquered by the euphoria of holding a baby for the first time. Having experienced that feeling three times in her life, it was now somewhat familiar to Bridget. But still, it was a feeling she could never get enough of. John was again at her side to share in the moment Sean was born, with tears in his eyes and a toothy grin upon his face. When they returned home to their farm after the birth, their lives picked up where they left off. Except there were now four of them – another mouth to feed, another soul to love. Bridget was busier and more sleep-deprived than ever, caring for a newborn and an energetic toddler. But it was fine. Being a wife and a mother to two beautiful children was all she could have ever asked for.

Four years passed. As did four Christmas mornings of unwrapping presents. Four birthdays, each with a little cake and candles that both Sean and Katy struggled to muster enough breath to blow out. Four years of scraped knees and cuts and bruises from climbing trees and exploring in the paddock. Four years of coughs and colds, nappy changes, dummy spits, play dates, tears, and laughter. They were still living on the farm in Wooroloo. Bridget was nursing on weekends at a retirement home, where she looked after old men and women, much like she looked after Sean and Katy (tantrums and nappy changes included). John worked as a truck driver Monday to Friday and looked after the kids on weekends. Money was tight, but love was always in abundance – and now Bridget discovered she was pregnant again, so they'd need as much of both as they could get.

Several months into her pregnancy, the day came that drew Bridget's mind away from the child within her back towards her firstborn in England. It was Reynagh's eighteenth birthday. And that meant there was no longer a legal barricade between them preventing them from being together. Reynagh was now able to search for her mother, if she wished. Bridget had always thought it was that clear-cut – that it was entirely and only up to Reynagh to arrange a reunion. That's what her social worker had drilled into her all those years ago. And that belief had stuck. So, when the day came, Bridget assumed she could merely wait and hope that she would get an answer to that question, which had nagged away at her for the better part of eighteen years. *Does Reynagh want to see me?*

The day came and went with no answer to that question. Then weeks passed and there was still no word from Reynagh. Not that Bridget was expecting there would be. Her firstborn may have legally been an adult, but she was still so young. It would have been incredibly daunting for her to reach out after so many years apart. She certainly wasn't expecting Reynagh to contact her. And even if she wanted to, what if she was unable to track Bridget down? As it always was, *hope* was the thing that allowed Bridget's sanity to remain.

That hope rose and fell, prospered and dwindled, but somehow it always remained as the years passed after Reynagh's birthday. Five years, in fact, went by. Bridget now had her hands full with three young children and a husband. Her relationship with John was not what it once was, though. He was getting home later and later from work each night, always with the strong smell of beer on his breath. He was talking less and shouting more. He was forever losing his temper, whether he was talking about his day at work – 'Fuckin' prick! Who does he think he is? I'll give him a piece of my mind' – or trying to fix something around the house – 'Jesus Christ! Why does nothing ever work around here?' – or if he'd downed enough beers, talking about his parents – 'My father was a drunken piece of shit ... My mother ... oh ... the oul bitch!'

Bridget feared that time would not heal the wounds John suffered in his childhood but rather make them fester. Their children, on the other hand, were very quickly growing up. Their daughter, Katy, was the extrovert – always talking, rarely behaving, but wildly entertaining. She dressed her younger brothers up as girls whenever she got the chance in an attempt to mask her disappointment at having little brothers instead of little sisters. She often threatened to run away from home when she got in trouble for misbehaving, like the many times she was shouted at for cutting the hair off her dolls and Barbies. Sean, the middle child, was the mild-mannered one. He was always the first to put his hand up to help his parents with chores around the house. But he was also the most likely to claim 'I'm the boss' and bark out orders when playing with his siblings on the farm. The youngest child, Daniel, was the dreamer of the pack, with an imagination that ran faster than he ever would. He spent most of his time playing outside with his imaginary friends and self-invented games, when he wasn't following his older brother and sister around like an annoying yapping dog.

For all their differences, Katy, Sean, and Daniel shared one uniting commonality – they were the centre of their mother's universe, as she was to them. Everything Bridget did was for her children. All the hours she worked at the nursing home, all the time she spent slaving over a hot stove or cleaning the house, all the driving, all the consoling, all the advising, all the nagging, all the disciplining, all the praying ... everything. It was all for them. But, of course, there was another who occupied that space in Bridget's psyche for those she loved most. Reynagh. For all Bridget had seen first-hand of Katy, Sean, and Daniel's growth as children, she still barely knew anything about her firstborn. All she really knew was that Reynagh was a young adult, on the verge of her mid-twenties. That was it. Everything else was pure speculation, a mere dream, albeit a lovely one. More than twenty years had passed since Bridget last laid eyes on Reynagh. Two decades' worth of birthdays, Christmases, school plays, dances, graduations, meeting of boyfriends, giving of advice, arguments, hugs, kisses, and everything in between. All of it missed. She still thought about Reynagh every day, even after all these years. And with every thought of her, there was that unrelenting hope of a reunion. Whether faint or resilient, it was always there.

It was a Monday evening. The kids were in bed and John was sitting in front of the TV, beer in hand. Bridget was in the kitchen, washing up after dinner. Her hands were deep in the warm soapy water when the phone rang. She glanced at the clock. It was almost 10 p.m. It wasn't unusual to get a call this late. She was used to phone calls at all hours from family and friends in Ireland.

She wiped the suds from her hands and picked up the phone. 'Hello?' she said, expecting to hear her mother's voice down the line.

'Hello,' the voice of an unknown Englishwoman said. 'Who am I speaking with?'

'This is Bridget Donnelly. And you are?'

'My name is Judy Wilson. I'm ringing from London. Do you have a moment for me to ask you a few questions?'

'Ah ... no, sorry, it's quite late here. And I'm not interested in buying anything. Thank you—'

'Mrs Donnelly, this is actually very important.'

'Oh,' Bridget said, her heartbeat rapidly gathering intensity.

'Can you confirm,' the Englishwoman continued, 'that you lived in London in the early seventies?'

Bridget froze, a surge of heat filling her cheeks. She took a moment to answer, as though it was a question that required thought and not, in fact, a simple one.

'I did,' she said.

'And during that time,' the woman said, 'did you attend an institution in Epping? A mother and baby home.'

Bridget hadn't heard that term – 'mother and baby home' – in years. She stood in silence in the kitchen for a moment, unable to talk. Just the loud humming of the fridge motor combined with the muffled murmurs of the TV from the lounge filled the kitchen. But she could hear another noise, a loud thudding, reverberating in her ears. It took her a moment to realise it was from her beating heart.

'Yes,' she finally answered.

'Mrs Donnelly, can you confirm that you gave birth to a girl in Epping Hospital on the fifteenth of July, 1971?'

'Yes,' Bridget said in a voice so soft it was barely distinguishable.

'Can you tell me the name that you gave to the child?' the Englishwoman asked.

'Reynagh,' Bridget said. The very mention of her name made Bridget's jaw quiver.

'I've been hired to find you, Mrs Donnelly,' the woman said. 'I've also been told to advise you that Reynagh wishes to make contact.'

Bridget almost dropped the phone. The woman's words seemed to echo around her head without actually sinking in. She didn't smile; in fact, she didn't move. She was numb from head to toe. *This can't be real.*

'I said, she's willing to contact you,' the woman said again. 'Are you willing to take a phone call from her? But I must stress ... that's all it will be. She simply wants to speak to you over the phone.'

'Yes!' Bridget said, loud enough to wake up her children at the other side of the house. 'Oh Lord, yes. Yes. Yes. Yes. I'd love to!'

'Fantastic,' the woman said. 'Does this time of day suit you?'

'Oh sure,' Bridget said, pacing around the kitchen, tangling the phone cord in her wake. 'This time, *any* time! You just tell me the time and I'll be ready.'

'That's quite fine, Mrs Donnelly. We'll aim to schedule a call for this time of the day. You can expect to hear from her in the coming days.'

'Oh,' Bridget muttered, tangling the phone cord even further around her. 'Oh, that's grand. That's lovely. Brilliant. I'm sorry though, did you say *days*? She'll call in *days*?'

'That's right,' the woman said. 'Just keep an ear out for the phone around this time. I'm glad I found you, Mrs Donnelly.'

'Jaysus, thank you! Thank you very much! Thanks a million!'

'Goodbye, Mrs Donnelly,'

'Goodbye. Thank you! Thanks a million. Thanks again!'

The woman hung up, leaving Bridget in the silence of her kitchen. She untangled herself from the phone cord and dipped her hands back in the sudsy water, which was now cold. She resumed scrubbing grease from pots and pans. She couldn't think straight; she couldn't stay still. So she scrubbed, zealously, furiously, until her hands cramped, resembling crab claws, and her fingers were white and prune-like. The pots and pans, crockery, and cutlery were all spotless. Every surface in the kitchen was shining. But Bridget still couldn't stop pacing and wiping everything again for good measure. Her mind was pacing too. She pictured Reynagh as she remembered her – a smiling baby in Debra's arms. Reynagh hadn't yet spoken her first words back then. But now, in just a few days, Bridget would have a proper conversation with her. Adult to adult. Mother to daughter. There was so much to say, so many empty years to be filled in. And they'd be able to get started in just a few days.

Bridget spent the next few nights within earshot of the phone. Every time it rang, she answered as though Reynagh's voice would greet her. She couldn't mask the disappointment in her own voice when she discovered it wasn't her daughter in England. Whenever she dropped the kids off at school in the morning, she raced home, teetering above the speed limit (which was rare for the usually slow-driving Bridget). She felt compelled to be close to the phone at all times, just in case Reynagh called unexpectedly early. She lay awake at night, tossing and turning, staring at the ceiling, while John's heavy breath heaved alongside her. Her ears played tricks on her – she heard the phone ringing, even when it wasn't. When she did finally manage to fall asleep, she dreamed the phone was ringing, which made her suddenly wake. That was usually when the doubts crept in. *Has Reynagh changed her mind? Does she still want to talk to me?*

Ring. Ring. Ring. It was 10 p.m. on a Monday evening. Bridget rose from the couch, where John had fallen asleep an hour or so earlier. She rushed to the phone and picked it up, pressing her sweaty palm against it. She forced down a lump in her throat and answered.

'Hello?' she said, her voice on the verge of collapse.

Silence.

'Hello.' It was the voice of a young Englishwoman. Soft, delicate, and slightly high-pitched.

'Is that you...' Bridget said, while trying to steady her trembling hand. '... Reynagh?'

'Yes,' she said in her endearing English accent.

Bridget was in a dreamlike state. She had dreamed of this moment so many times before. Some of those dreams had been so realistic, almost to the point that she couldn't distinguish fact from fiction when she woke. But ironically now that it was *actually* happening, it didn't feel real. It was quite simply too good to be true. Reynagh must have been lost for words as well, so Bridget spoke next.

'How are you?' Bridget asked, as though inquiring about someone's day in a casual greeting, not catching up on more than twenty years of lost memories.

'I'm good, thanks,' Reynagh answered. Her voice was so soft, so quiet. She sounded nervous.

'Thank you, Reynagh,' Bridget said spontaneously.

'Why are you thanking me?'

'For *this*,' Bridget said. 'For getting in touch. I've waited so long for this day.'

'So have I,' Reynagh responded. 'I'm just glad you wanted to talk to me as well.'

'Oh Jesus!' Bridget said, gasping. 'Of course I do. I've *always* wanted to, dear.'

She had to stop talking at the risk of getting too emotional. She took a deep breath before continuing. 'There's so much I've wanted to say to you, love. So much you deserve to know. I'm sure you've got loads of questions for me as well. How much time do you have to talk?'

'Plenty,' Reynagh said.

They spoke for ages. Bridget wasn't quite sure how long. She'd lost track of time in her dreamlike state of euphoria. Thankfully, she was no longer the shy and quiet girl she had once been. These days she was easily able to hold down conversations, sometimes two or three of them at the same time. So Bridget did most of the talking. She asked Reynagh all about her life in England. There was so much to hear about – Reynagh's adoptive family, her childhood, her friends, her schooling years, and now her life as a young woman. With every word Reynagh spoke,

Bridget was learning more about her. Her daughter sounded like a bubbly, confident young woman, with 'loads of friends', a good job at a bank in London, and a 'drop-dead-gorgeous man' at her side. Reynagh spoke of her love for the London nightlife, meeting new people, making new friends, much like Bridget did all those years ago. She spoke very fondly of her childhood with Rob and Debra and her brothers and sisters. Aside from asking a barrage of questions, Bridget also spoke of Katy, Sean, Daniel, and John.

Reynagh responded to every bit of information with a high-pitched 'Oh that's so lovely ... I've got another sister ... and a brother ... and *another* brother. They sound so sweet – my little Aussie family!' The conversation was but a tiny glimpse into each other's lives – more than twenty years condensed into phone chitchat. But they couldn't talk all night, so the call unwillingly came to an end.

'I'm so glad you found me,' Bridget said again.

'So am I,' Reynagh said. 'Maybe we can ... have a little chat again some time.'

'Of course!' Bridget said. '*Any* time, dear.'

'Okay, I better be going,' Reynagh said softly, almost apologetically. 'It's been great to finally talk to you. Goodbye.'

'Goodbye, Reynagh. I love you.'

Beeping filled the earpiece. The call had ended. But something else had begun – a new life for Bridget, one that featured Reynagh within it, even if it was only through an international phone call. But now at least she knew the sound of her firstborn's voice. She knew she had lots of friends, and a loving family, and a boyfriend, and a good job, and was enjoying the colourful nightlife in London. Bridget didn't have to imagine the existence of those things any more, for she'd heard it directly from Reynagh. In a way, she was content to have simply spoken to her. But in another way, she yearned to hear her delicate English voice again, to actually see her, to put a face to the voice, to be in the same room as her, to hold her in her arms once more.

Several weeks later, after dropping the kids off at school, Bridget was sifting through the mail when she found a handwritten letter among the regular pile of bills.

Dear Bridget,

It has been a long time since we last spoke. But I've thought of you many times over the years. I'm so happy that Reynagh was able to find you. She was over the moon. She is a wonderful young woman and the joy of our lives. It was also wonderful to hear that you now have a family of your own. We wish you all the best. I have sent you some photos of Reynagh as a child. I hope looking at them brings you happiness.

Kind regards,

Debra.

Bridget folded the letter and retrieved a bunch of photos from within the envelope. The first was of Reynagh as a toddler, resembling a slightly bigger version of the baby Bridget had last laid eyes on. She was probably about two years old, standing in just her shorts, a guilty look and smear of chocolate upon her face. In the next photo, Reynagh was probably about five or six years old. She was wearing a grey dress that hung down to her shins, black stockings, and a grey jumper. It must have been her school uniform. There was a school bag, about half the size of her, hanging over her shoulder. Perhaps it was her first day of school. She had a huge grin, revealing a large gap where her front tooth had fallen out. The next photo was of her frolicking in the snow with several older children, most likely her brothers and sisters. Her smile was once again brimming across her face. Bridget brushed her fingers against the glossy surface of the photo, imagining the sound of Reynagh laughing with her siblings. She flicked through to the final photo. A slightly older Reynagh was staring up at her. She would have been in her late teens. She was wearing a black-and-blue ball gown with frills around the arms and waist. A large bow was sitting on her head among a mop of thick curly black hair. She was most likely about to go to her high school prom. She had grown so much compared to the girl in the previous photos, but her smile was just as infectiously heart-warming. Bridget flicked through the precious snapshots again and again, her eyes scanning over every little detail – it felt like Reynagh was growing up before her very eyes. Bridget was so thankful that Debra had given her this opportunity.

The letters from Debra kept coming as the months passed, as did the photos. Bridget and Reynagh spoke over the phone several more times as well. Hearing her voice, seeing pictures of her as a cheeky kid and now a smiling young woman – it made Bridget feel a part of Reynagh's life for the first time in more than twenty years. After those decades of feeling robbed of her presence, she was now discovering *who* Reynagh was, more and more with every phone call, letter, and photo. Reynagh was a kind and caring soul, beginning every conversation with a flamboyant 'Hellooo!' and always asking how Bridget and her family were doing. She hung on every bit of news Bridget delivered, constantly responding with 'Oh that's lovely' in her high-pitched English twang. She asked so many questions, and was always more than happy to answer any Bridget had of her. She also spoke fondly of her childhood and her adoptive family. She often laughed and joked during their lengthy chats. She never seemed bitter or resentful for having been given away. From these phone calls alone, Bridget realised that Reynagh had become the woman she'd always wanted her to be: a young woman who would make any mother proud.

Three months had passed since they first spoke when Bridget received another letter. Her name and address were neatly handwritten on the front, with a return address in London printed on the back. Assuming it was another letter from Debra, she quickly tore it open, hoping to find a new batch of pictures inside. But there were no photos in the envelope. There was just a handwritten letter, which she read aloud.

Dear (G'day) Bridget,

It's been so nice speaking to you these last few months. I'm writing to you hoping that we can speak again. But instead of doing it over the phone, I'd really like to be able to speak to you in person.

My parents and I are going to make the trip to Australia early next year. It looks so beautiful over there, with all them lovely beaches and that perfect sunny weather. It will be a nice change from the bloody rain here in London. It never stops!

We haven't booked our tickets yet. But we're aiming for February some time. I would really love to meet you after all this time. It would be great to meet John and your children as well. Let me know if you also want to meet me. I'll understand if it's too difficult for you, after everything you've been through. Looking forward to hearing from you.

With love,

Reynagh.

CHAPTER EIGHTEEN

WHOLE AGAIN

Waiting. Bridget spent most of her life waiting for something. Waiting for children to clean their rooms, waiting for pay day, waiting for her mother to call from Ireland, waiting for her twelve-hour shift at the nursing home to finish. But this was entirely different. There was no wait that could compare to this. Reynagh was coming to Australia. Bridget would finally get to see her, to hold her, just as she had all those years ago in the mother and baby home. But before that could happen, she had to break the news to John, Sean, Katy, and Daniel.

John was the easiest to tell. After all, he already knew about Reynagh.

'Oh, that's nice,' he said casually while chewing on his steak when Bridget told him about the letter.

But Bridget feared telling her children wouldn't go as smoothly. She broke the news to Katy and Sean first, who were ten and nine years old at the time. The conversation was forced upon her when the kids noticed her on the phone to Reynagh one day when they were talking about the upcoming reunion. Bridget hadn't realised just how excited she must have seemed during that call until she hung up and was greeted by Katy and Sean with, 'What is it, Mum? What is it? Who you were speaking to just then? Tell us! Tell us! Please! What are you so excited about?'

'Well, kids,' Bridget said, hesitating. 'The thing is ... that was my ... daughter. Your sister.'

'What?' Katy said. 'Are you serious? Oh my God! I have a sister! I have a sister! Oh my God. Yes!'

'Sean,' Bridget said. 'How do you feel about that?'

Sean took a moment to answer. 'That's awesome!' he finally said. 'When can we meet her?'

'She's coming to Australia very soon. That's actually what I was just speaking to her about. She can't wait to—'

'When?' Katy cut in. 'I'm coming. I have to meet her! I can't believe I've finally got a sister! I have a sister! Yay!'

Bridget's youngest child, Daniel, was only five years old. He was playing with his toy cars in the lounge room when she called him over to share the news.

'I've got something to tell you,' Bridget said, picking him up and placing him on her knee.

'What?' Daniel asked, innocently.

'Well, Danny. The thing is ... well ... how would you feel if I told you that you have *another* sister.'

'Umm,' Daniel muttered, scratching his head. 'Good.'

'Her name is Reynagh,' Bridget said. 'She was in my tummy a long time ago. Back when I lived in London, in England. That was a long time before you were born, Danny. But I was very young back then. I was actually too young to be Reynagh's mummy. So we found another mummy and daddy for her. They're also from

England. And that's where they've been living, as a big happy family. But now they're coming all the way here to Australia. And they want to meet me, and you, and Katy, and Sean, and your dad as well. What do you think about that?'

'Hmm, it's good,' the little boy said, not flinching in the slightest at the gravity of the revelation. 'Can I please go back to playing with my cars?'

'Go on then,' Bridget said, smirking.

In the months following Reynagh's letter, Bridget was as busy as she had always been – looking after her three children, nursing, cooking, cleaning, plus all the other demands that came with being a mother and wife. She was incredibly busy in that time. But essentially, she was just waiting. Waiting for her past to emerge in her present. And just as was the case all those years ago in the mother and baby home, time was unforgiving. The days dragged along, passing painfully slowly, turning into weeks, then months, until the day finally arrived – six months after Reynagh wrote her letter, and more than twenty years after Bridget had handed her over to Debra in Nottingham.

Bridget couldn't sleep the night before. She tossed and turned within her sheets, but sleep never found her. She was still wide awake in the morning, despite her bloodshot eyes and the heavy dark bags under them. Her stomach churned as she fixed breakfast for the kids. She felt too nervous to eat anything herself. Once the boys were showered and dressed, she dropped them off at school. Katy had refused to go to school when she'd found out Reynagh was coming.

'I want to meet my sister! I want to meet my sister! I want to meet my sister!' She had kept yelling that until Bridget finally caved and allowed her to have the day off.

After dropping the boys off at school, Bridget, John, and Katy piled into the well-weathered green family van. John was driving, Bridget in the front seat, Katy in the back. They set off along the gravel road they lived on in Wooroloo, the wheels crackling as they rolled over the brown dirt and rocks. The engine roared as it always did, revving furiously like a rundown lawnmower. Bridget stared out the window as the thick sprawling bush gradually dwindled away, becoming sparse, while the houses and buildings along the roads became more frequent as they drew closer to the city. It would take about an hour to get to the meeting point – a motel in the heart of Perth where Reynagh was staying with Rob and Debra.

No one spoke a word during the car ride. Bridget couldn't even look at John or Katy. Her knee was rapidly bouncing up and down, her eyes focused solely out the window. Nerves are sometimes described as butterflies in the stomach. To Bridget, it felt more like a swarm of angry locusts, frantically buzzing around her belly. But her fidgeting and inner tingles were nothing compared to what was happening in her head. *What if it doesn't go well? What if Reynagh has felt rejected all these years? She probably hates me for what I've done to her. She grew up knowing her birth mother had given her away. What if she was teased in school? Did nasty kids say to her 'That's not your real mum' when Debra used to pick her up? She probably resents me. She's always been the 'adopted child' because of me. She probably looked different to her brothers and sisters, to Rob and Debra. What if she felt like an outsider in her own family? She probably doesn't want a relationship with me now. I mean, where do I even fit in her life? She has a mother already. Maybe Debra will feel like she's been replaced if I'm back in Reynagh's life. And Reynagh is such a kind soul; she would never want to hurt Debra's feelings. Maybe she'll just turn her back on me to be with Debra instead. I mean, all I'll do is complicate her life. Plus, Reynagh has no memory of me. She was too young to remember our time together. But I remember it all so vividly, as though it happened yesterday. I've mourned her, the baby she was. I'll never hold that baby again. But maybe, hopefully, I'll get to hold the woman she is now. That's all I can do I guess – hope beyond hope that she will love me back. Maybe she won't. Maybe she'll turn around after seeing me and return to England, never to speak to me again. Maybe. Who knows? Whatever happens though, it can't be worse than a life of 'what ifs'.*

Bridget's erratic thoughts were interrupted when she noticed a florist up ahead on the roadside.

'Can you please pull over?' she asked John.

It was the first time anyone had spoken since they had left the house half an hour earlier. John obliged, pulling to the side of the busy four-lane road. It didn't take Bridget long to find what she was looking for inside the florist. A small bouquet of pink roses. She pressed the flowers against her nose, taking in the sweet scent. How fitting, she thought. *Beautiful roses, for my beautiful English rose.*

Flowers in hand, Bridget arrived at the destination. John stopped the van outside the modest motel. It was a relatively dull cream-coloured two-storey building that was stained with orange water marks. John idled the engine and turned to Bridget.

'You go in,' he said. 'Me and Katy will just take a little drive. We'll come back and see you later. After you've had some time with her by yourself.'

'Thanks,' Bridget said, clutching John's hand before getting out of the van. It crawled away down the road and out of sight, the rumbling drone of engine in its wake. She stood in front of the motel, her feet frozen to the footpath. She took a folded piece of paper from her jacket pocket. She stared at it for a moment, memorising the room number. *Five six eight three. Five six eight three. Five six eight three.* She passed the unmanned front office and climbed a dingy and dark concrete stairwell. She paced down a hallway, passing room after room. It felt like she'd passed every room in the building before she finally came to the door she was looking for: 5683. She lingered in front of the door, anxiously pulling the piece of paper from her pocket to check again that this was the right room number. She clenched her hand into a fist, hovering it in front of the door in readiness to knock. Her hand was trembling; in fact, her whole body was shaking. Quite visibly as well. It would be impossible to hide this when the door opened. She knocked three times and waited.

There was a rustling of noise from within the room: the movement of feet and several hushed voices. The door creaked, then gradually, almost slow-motion-like, swung open. But it wasn't Reynagh standing in the doorway. It was a man Bridget had never seen before. He was tall with white hair, a goatee, and large golden spectacles. Her heart dropped. Maybe her fears had been realised. Maybe Reynagh *had* changed her mind.

'Hello there,' he said cheerfully.

'Oh ... hello,' Bridget said. 'Sorry, I think I've got the wrong room.'

'I'm Rob,' he said, holding out his hand.

'Oh, Rob. Oh, Jesus. Lovely to meet you. Lord above, I'm sorry if I looked shocked to see ye when you opened the door. I'm Bridget.'

They stood opposite each other for a moment, awkwardly smiling, before Rob politely filled the silence.

'There's a lovely little garden downstairs in the foyer courtyard. There's a bench as well you can sit on. How about you wait down there for a few minutes? Reynagh won't be too far away. She's still getting ready.'

'Of course, no bother,' Bridget said, heading for the courtyard. 'Thanks a million, Rob. 'Twas lovely to meet ye.'

The little garden was situated in the middle of the complex, with the motel rooms surrounding it like an atrium. It was a poor excuse for a garden, really. The grass was tinged with brown patches that had been scorched by the summer sun. There were a few small trees and native shrubs that looked like they hadn't been groomed in years. And there was a crumbling red footpath that led to the surrounding rooms. It was the sort of place where motel guests usually came to smoke half a pack of cigarettes (as was clear by all the cigarette butts covering the ground), rather than reuniting with long-lost family members. But still, none of that mattered to Bridget. This was as good a place as any to reunite with her girl.

She sat on the bench, foot tapping frantically, eyes darting, heart pounding, and, of course, cheeks burning. She couldn't sit still. She couldn't think straight. Her entire body was tingling, like she was intoxicated by adrenaline. Adrenaline that had been born out of two decades of anticipation. All those years, the world was between them. So many precious moments had become memories, in which they did not feature together. But that was about to change. They were about to create new memories together for the first time since Reynagh was a baby. The wind picked up, rustling through the trees in the courtyard as the tip of the sun appeared over the top of the motel's tin roof. She stared at the empty footpath that led towards Reynagh's room. In just a few minutes, she would walk along that path, unless she changed her mind.

Bridget thought back to the last time she saw her. It was at the adoption agency in Nottingham, where she met with Debra and made the adoption official. Bridget was a broken young woman back then, resigned to the fact she was signing her life away. Despair had its cold grip on her during that meeting. But somehow, strangely, she felt a little spark, a glimmer of hope, a silver lining to all the loss and sadness. And it struck her when she saw baby Reynagh smiling in Debra's arms. Seeing that was enough for Bridget to sweep aside her personal desires to keep Reynagh as her own and dive headfirst into an uncertain future together.

Her memories then took her back to her time in the mother and baby home. Their precious six weeks together after the birth, albeit within a melting pot of unmarried mothers and their newborns and the callous Reverend Mother and the other nuns. It was a wonderful time of bonding. It was also a terribly frightening time, as a looming deadline closed in. But the fond memories of the mother and baby home were the ones Bridget held onto. The memories with Reynagh in the nursery: the early morning nappy changes, and baths, and hugs and kisses, and singing in unison with the other mothers while the dawn broke outside.

She then thought back to the time she carried Reynagh within her. She was hidden beneath her skin, as well as abundant layers of loose clothing. But Bridget could *feel* her – her little kicks, her rolling, even just the weight of her. She was a part of Bridget, not just physically. It eventually became a missing part. But now, as Bridget sat on the bench of the motel courtyard, in the poor excuse for a garden, on the opposite side of the world from London, everything was about to change.

The patter of footsteps came from the opposite side of the courtyard. Bridget cast her eyes towards it, and there she was. It was Reynagh, all grown up with shoulder-length curly black hair that was glistening in the Aussie sun. Her big brown eyes locked with Bridget's for a moment, and in that moment, *time*, that dreaded thing, which had been so cruel and unforgiving over the years, seemed to finally show some mercy. It stopped. At least, that's how it felt to Bridget as she and her firstborn looked at each other. Reynagh was glowing, her sun-kissed olive skin appearing to emanate an air of radiance around her. She stood on the edge of the poor excuse of a garden, clasping her hands to her mouth. Debra and Rob were standing a few feet behind her, watching on, supporting their girl.

Bridget rose from the bench, leaving the bouquet of flowers behind. Her legs were unsteady, the muscles in them jelly-like. Her vision blurred as her eyes filled with tears. Reynagh was also crying. Droplets were rolling down her face, passing over her infectious grin. She slowly walked towards Bridget, with Rob and Debra not far behind. But Bridget was stuck on the spot, transfixed on the young woman in front of her, as though an angel had descended from heaven and was approaching. She forced herself to take a step. *I'm dreaming.* Another step. *This isn't real.* Another step. *She's so beautiful.* Another step. *Thank you.* Another step. *My beautiful girl.*

Bridget stretched out her arms. Reynagh did the same, and they embraced. Bridget felt the warmth of her touch, the floral scent of her perfume, the soft sounds of her whimpering. It was a hug unlike any she'd experienced – it was so warm and tight, it felt like it would never end. It felt like every missed hug over the years had been saved up and crammed into this one. They both sobbed their hearts out into the warm embrace of each other's shoulders. They smiled, they even laughed as they held each other for who knows how long, but they barely said a word. None were needed. Rob and Debra stood a few feet away, their arms around each other, tears on their cheeks and smiles upon their faces. Bridget felt everything darken around her and Reynagh, becoming empty, an abyss, as though there was nothing else in the world at this moment, no one else – just the two of them, back together.

Bridget was finally whole again.

PRESENT

CHAPTER NINETEEN

BYE BABY

I'm driving home from work, but I'm stuck in traffic during afternoon rush hour. A pile of papers is sitting next to me on the front passenger's seat. There are several hundred pages covered in words, which I'd printed earlier in the day. The culmination of the last two years is inked on each of these pages. That's how long it's been since I first sat down with Mum at her kitchen table, when we started this journey together. It's hard to believe I barely knew anything about her story back then. Now I feel as though I know it so well, I was there as it happened, watching from afar. It's felt like a long two years, filled with many teary conversations and sleepless nights. I sometimes thought we might not get to this point, especially during the moments Mum seemed overcome with despair when recounting her story. In those moments, when her voice cut out and tears flowed, I didn't want to keep going. I didn't want to see her that way any more – consumed with the pain of her past. But Mum was always adamant. 'We need to keep going,' she'd say. 'I have to do this. For my healing ... for the other mothers.' And she did.

The main road I'm on is three lanes wide, but it resembles a car park. Traffic stretches as far as I can see before the road bends away to the right. There must be a crash up ahead, or a broken-down truck or something. I'll probably be sitting here for a while. I'd usually be annoyed by this after an epic day in the newsroom when all I want to do is get home. But today, traffic suits me just fine. It gives me time to properly think for the first time all day (without the chaos of the newsroom to distract me). I stare at the pile of papers on the passenger seat, which I'll hand over to Mum in a few days when I see her next. My mind drifts to the people who shaped the words on these pages. For some reason, the Christian Brothers come to mind first.

Yep, those white-robed so-called Men of God who supposedly 'looked after' Dad and other child migrants when they first came to Australia. I'm sure most of the Christian Brothers who tormented children like my father have already gone to their graves. Part of me wishes they were still alive so I could track them down and give them a piece of my mind – and a fist to the face. I bet they'd cower when confronted as old men, when confronted by an adult, when confronted by anyone who isn't a vulnerable child under their care. I generally think the idea of people being holistically good or evil is bullshit. Humans are complicated, and there's generally some good and bad in most of us. But the Christian Brothers, the ones who abused orphaned children, *are* evil. They have caused generations of immeasurable hurt. Not just to the children they abused, but also their victims' families and friends later in life. Even though I don't believe it, I hope there is a God, the same God the Christian Brothers claimed to serve, so that he/she can judge them in death for their abhorrent crimes in life.

I think about the nuns, the Reverend Mother, the social workers. Each of them played a role in judging my mother and forcing her down the path of adoption. Maybe they were doing what they thought was right. I don't know. I'd like to think their horrible mistreatment wasn't driven by malice, but rather ignorance, even arrogance. That by no means excuses the way they treated Mum, and all the other unmarried mothers of that era. It was then, and is now, completely inexcusable. It's also somewhat ironic that their condemnation of unmarried mothers was done in the name of pride, yet the condemning itself worthy of none. I just hope those of them who are still alive can have the chance to change – or at least realise they were wrong in their mistreatment of vulnerable women. If not, at least my generation and generations to come can learn from the mistakes of the past.

I think about Dad and the role he played in Mum's story. I regret that I've learnt more about my father while writing this book than I did while he was alive. I regret not spending more time with him when he was alive, even when he seemed perpetually angry at the world around him. I wish his life didn't have to end in the way it did, just as we were starting to rebuild a relationship, and before he had the chance to make amends with Mum. But to me, Dad's memory is so much more than the misery he was dealt in life. His memory is one of love. He loved his children, his grandchildren, his brothers and sisters, animals, music, and his lifelong mates. And he loved my mother, despite everything he put her through, despite their bitter breakup and years of estrangement that followed, despite everything, he still loved her. I'm sure of it. I like to believe that all the hatred and pain in his life died when he did, and now *love* is all that remains.

I think of Reynagh, my beautiful sister. I can't imagine how she felt all those years, knowing she was given up for adoption and dealing with all the unanswered questions that came with it. After reuniting, Mum apologised to Reynagh for giving her up. She asked for forgiveness. But Reynagh said there was nothing to forgive. 'You gave me life,' she told Mum. 'That's the best gift anyone could give.' There was no resentment, no anger; there was nothing but appreciation. Reynagh truly is an amazing woman. I hope the words on the pages sitting next to me can show her how much she was loved by her mother from the day she was born. And that love, the colossal love of a mother for her firstborn, will never cease to exist.

I think about Mum, whose tears and laughter, joy and despair, love and loss form the very foundations of the pages sitting next to me. I'm so proud of her for wanting to share her story with the world after keeping it hidden for so long. I've seen her cry more during the past two years than I have in my entire lifetime. It's made me realise that Mum *never* got over the pain of losing Reynagh and the guilt that came with it. I was naïve to think she ever had. She still carries the burden, an incurable illness usually hidden within, even after forty years. But I think what makes her so amazing is the person she's become, despite the pain she's endured. She has been the most caring, loving, generous, fierce, and inspirational mother to Katy, Sean, and me. And she's done it despite experiencing the hardest loss and inconsolable guilt one could imagine. I am so lucky to have her as my mother.

And finally, my mind turns to the inspiration behind the pages sitting next to me. The reason Mum wanted to share her story in the first place – to help other unmarried mothers. I have heard the most horrific stories during the past two years. Women who were raped or abandoned or alone, cast away by their families, tormented in mother and baby homes, forced to part with their babies and sentenced to a life of incompleteness with a part of them eternally missing. Sadly, many of those women have never had the chance to meet their children as adults. And some who've had reunions have not been able to rekindle the mother–child relationship as they remembered it. I hope those unmarried mothers who are still here can find some comfort in Mum's story – whether it shows them they are not forgotten, or simply that they're loved and respected. But mostly, I hope it shows them that they have nothing to be ashamed of.

There's a beep from behind me, which instantly plugs my steady stream of thoughts. I put my foot to the accelerator. The traffic has lifted, creating a steady path home.

I open the door of my apartment, the pile of papers tucked away neatly within the bag slung over my shoulder. My girlfriend, Jen, is sitting on the couch, eyes on me as though they've been fixed on the door for hours, waiting for me to walk through it.

'I'm going to ruin your day,' she says, her voice quivering.

She picks up a small white strip of plastic from her bag. It's a familiar-looking little stick, but one I've only seen before in movies.

'You're pregnant?' I say, the words slipping out of my mouth before I have the chance to comprehend them.

'Yep,' she says, tears welling in her eyes.

What? I'm lost for words, thoughts too. My mouth hangs open like a thirsty dog. I'm just staring at the little bit of plastic in Jen's hands, utterly dumbstruck.

'Are you serious?' I say. 'You're not just trying to stir me up, are you?'

We're always playing little jokes on each other. *Surely that's just what this is. I mean, this can't be real.*

'Nope, I'm pregnant,' she says again.

She hands me the pregnancy test, which has two red lines running across its flat surface. One of the red lines is slightly fainter than the other, like it's been printed with a near-empty cartridge. That must be the pregnancy line – the line that's been magically changing people's lives in an instant, ever since these little tests were invented.

I sit on the couch and put my arm around Jen, pulling her in for a hug. 'It's going to be alright,' I say.

I'm not sure if that's true. I'm not sure of *anything* at the moment, to be honest.

'This is just the worst timing,' she says. 'I mean, I'm about to start a new job … we live in an apartment the size of a shoebox … we've got no money.'

'Yeah, it's not *great* timing,' I say.

I sit in silence as I try to gather my thoughts. But there are no thoughts in my mind. There's nothing at all. The shock seems to have shorted my internal wiring, rendering my brain incapable of doing its most basic task – thinking.

'What are you thinking?' Jen asks, giving me a concerned look.

'Ahhh,' I say. 'I dunno … I just … yeah … I don't know *what* to think. How are you?'

'About the same,' she says. 'I did the test at work. I wanted to ring you straight away but I didn't want to disturb you in the office. It was the longest bloody three hours. I couldn't think straight, so I just told the boss I was sick and came home.'

Jen reaches for her laptop on the coffee table. 'Want to see something crazy?' she says.

'Ah ... okay?'

Jen opens the laptop and shows me a diagram of what looks like a small slug. 'That's what it looks like,' she says. 'It's about five millimetres long ... the size of a sesame seed.'

'Holy shit! It looks more tadpole than human!'

'Its heart is starting to beat already,' she says.

Heart? Beating? Already? I picture the little slug-shaped, five-millimetre-long, tadpole-looking thing with a beating heart. We created this thing. But seeing it doesn't make it feel any less surreal.

We hug again, holding on to each other for a few minutes, drowning in the silence. My mind, which has been full of thoughts all afternoon about the book and all who shaped it, is now, quite simply, empty.

As days pass, I almost feel a bit guilty. Some people try for years to get pregnant and it just doesn't happen. But it just happened for us, right when we didn't ask it to. Jen and I are still so young. Too young to be parents. We're only twenty-eight. That's young, right? Right? Shit, maybe it's not *that* young. But I'm not ready for this. Jen's not ready. We're *both* not ready. We rent a tiny apartment in the city, we're not married, and we can't get a mortgage at the moment. Plus, we want to enjoy a few more years of our lives with it just being the two of us. Maybe we can sneak in a little bit more travelling, fancy dinners, and nights out with friends before a baby comes along. The timing is just ... wrong. But is anyone really ever *ready* for a baby? People often seem to either have a little accident and fall pregnant, and it's too soon, or they try and try and try and can't get pregnant, and it's too late. Is there ever really a right time when money isn't a problem, when careers and housing situations and life ambitions are just perfectly in place for a little one to come along? I don't know. It's been days since I found out we're having a baby, and I still don't know anything. As far as expecting fathers go, I feel pretty clueless. So I head down to the bookstore and buy a doorstopper-sized pregnancy manual. I also Google the shit out of everything pregnancy-related, stumbling across some disturbing childbirth photos in the process. I still feel clueless, but at least there's no shortage of information to guide me on my path of cluelessness.

A few weeks after we found out, we go for a scan to find out if the little bit of white plastic with two red lines on it was right – if our lives really are about to change forever. We sit in the waiting room of the ultrasound clinic as heavily pregnant women walk in and out of the front reception. One of them, a woman in her mid-thirties with a huge bump, is with her husband and their child – a boy who's probably three or four years old. He seems to be pretty well behaved as he plays on his mother's phone while they wait for their appointment. But then, when his mother's name is called, she grabs her phone off the little boy and horror ensues – a red-faced toddler tantrum of tears, clenched fists, and high-pitched wailing. Seeing this screaming child a few months ago would have been a good contraceptive – a reminder to be more careful so we don't create our own snotty-faced, screaming toddler to worry about. Too late now for a warning from the universe, I guess.

We're called into a private room. Jen lies up on the bed while I sit next to her in what must typically be the fathers' chair, or chair for whoever is supporting the mum-to-be. The sonographer, a woman in her late thirties, squeezes some jelly onto Jen's stomach, just like I've seen so many times in the movies. She presses the ultrasound device to Jen's abdomen, searching for signs of life. I'm suddenly terrified that she'll find nothing and we won't be having a baby after all. I look at Jen and I'm pretty sure she's thinking the same thing.

'There we are,' the sonographer says. 'That's baby, right there.'

Jen and I stare at the screen in front of us. Goosebumps seem to instantly cover my arms, even though I don't really know what I'm looking at. All that fills the screen is a jellybean-shaped shadow with a flickering light in the middle of it.

'That's the heartbeat,' the sonographer says. 'Everything looks pretty good. I'll just give bub a measure and see how it's tracking.'

She hits some buttons and measures our little jellybean-shaped shadow.

'Baby is about seventeen millimetres,' she says. 'Which means you're about eight weeks pregnant.'

We both stare at the image of our little baby. Seventeen millimetres! It's so tiny – about the size of a raspberry, but still much bigger than the sesame seed we had a couple of weeks ago. It's such a miniscule thing, yet it fills the screen in front of us and will most definitely fill our lives until our dying days. Jen and I tear our eyes away from the screen for a moment to look at each other. We're both smiling. Our little surprise has now become our overwhelming joy.

After the scan, we realise that it's official – we're having a baby. So, it's time we start telling those closest to us. Jen rings her mum and aunty, who live on the other side of the country, to break the news. They are ecstatic and shed tears of joy, just as she expected they would. Now all we have to do is tell Mum. I know I can talk to her about pretty much anything. But I'm still nervous to break this news to her.

A few days after the scan, we're at Mum's place for a visit when we decide to make the announcement.

Jen and I look at each other, a few hours into our visit, as we drink tea at the kitchen table. She gives me a look, with raised eyebrows, that seems to say 'It's time.' *Okay! Here we go.*

Mum is on the couch, reading a book. I sit next to her while Jen sits alongside me on the armrest.

'Mum,' I say. 'Umm ... you know how things just ... *happen*, in life sometimes?'

She looks up from her book and snaps it shut. 'Oh,' she says, in her high-pitched Irish twang. 'Do you have some *good* news for me?'

'I suppose ... thing is ... we're having a baby.'

Mum springs up from the sofa as though her lotto numbers have just come up (she's eternally dreaming of that day), a beaming grin, her arms outstretched towards us.

'I can't believe it,' she says. 'Come here! Come here!' She wraps Jen and me in an engulfing hug. 'Oh my God,' she says. 'This is wonderful!' She's pacing around on the spot, unable to stay still, just like an excited puppy. 'I can't believe we're going to have a new bubby in the family!'

'Yeah, it's exciting,' I say. 'But it's pretty scary. Obviously, we didn't plan this.'

'Oh, don't ye be worrying about that. This is wonderful!'

'Thanks, Bridget,' Jen says. 'It's still a bit of a shock, but we're very happy.'

'Yeah ... and I'm a bit clueless,' I say. 'I bought a book to try and get my head around it.'

'Don't ye be worrying with books,' Mum says. 'You'll know what to do when the time comes. You'll just learn as you go. Don't be wasting your money on books.'

We all sit back down, but Mum is still shuffling in the chair, like an overly excited kid. Her eyes are glistening under the golden lights. She's definitely more excited than Jen and I were when we found out.

'You're going to be a daddy, Dan. And Jen, you're going to be a mummy.'

It feels strange hearing those words being said out loud. But strange in a good way, an unexpectedly thrilling way.

I can't believe how well Mum's taken the news. Not that I ever doubted she'd take it well. But despite her strict Catholic faith, she doesn't seem to care at all that Jen and I are having a child while unmarried.

I don't know how Mum got through it all by herself back in London when she fell pregnant with Reynagh. Jen and I are in our late twenties – we have good jobs, support from our families and friends, and a plethora of information about pregnancy and childbirth available to us. But we're *still* terrified. Mum had none of the support that we have when she fell pregnant with Reynagh. Worse than that, she had to deal with judgement from so many people around her. But she somehow got through it and gave birth to a beautiful little girl.

I'm so fortunate to have a mother that's so supportive of Jen and me in this situation. Because I know that even today, this sort of conversation would be very different in some other households. Instead of excitement and support, the focus of the baby revelation would be 'How are we going to fix this? What will other people say? How quickly can we arrange a wedding?'

How lucky am I? Sitting here with my beautiful partner next to me, our baby growing within her, who we both can't wait to meet. And on my other side, my mother, Bridget, whose face is drenched in joy – the happiest I've seen her in years. And she keeps saying the same thing, over and over again …

'It's a miracle.'

Thank you so much for reading!

You can get touch with Bridget and Daniel through email or social media. They'd love to hear from you.

byebaby@byebabybook.com
https://www.facebook.com/byebabybook
www.byebabybook.com

And if you loved the book, we'd really appreciate it if you could share the love by posting about it on social media, using: **#byebabybook**

Printed in Great Britain
by Amazon